Get a Good Deal on Your

Health Insurance

Without Getting Ripped-Off

by

Jonathan Pletzke

Aji Publishing

Aji Publishing
P.O. Box 2207
Chapel Hill, North Carolina 27515-2207
www.AjiBooks.com

Discounts are available on quantity purchases.
Custom versions of this book and excerpts are also available for your organization.
Contact Aji Publishing at 919-338-1863 or quantity@AjiBooks.com.

ISBN: 978-0-9794-7810-9

LCCN: 2007905959

Please visit our website for more information and updates at:
www.BestHealthInsuranceBook.com.

Type and Design Consultant: John Labovitz

Cover Designer: Heather Herndon

Table of Contents

Table of Figures

Disclaimer

This book is written for informational and educational purposes. Neither the author nor the publisher of this book is in the business of providing legal, financial, or other professional services or advice. As such, neither the author nor the publisher can be liable for your actions due to reading this book. You should contact competent professional advisors before making decisions about what is best for you. The author and publisher specifically disclaim any personal liability, loss or risk incurred as a consequence of the use and application, either directly or indirectly, of any information presented herein. All trademarks mentioned are the property of their respective owners. Any similarity of fictional persons in this book to actual persons living or dead is purely coincidental.

Acknowledgments

The following people were kind enough to take time out of their busy schedules for this project. Without their help, this book would not exist. They have my most heartfelt thanks. Jennifer McLaurin (Director of Sales, J.F. Sipp & Associates) helped me throughout the process of writing this book and reviewed the book to spot errors. Lauren Gadkowski Lindsay (CFP, NAPFA Registered Financial Advisor, Personal Financial Advisors) shared insights into HSA's and the role of insurance in a financial plan. Dianne Lawton (former Director of Individual Sales, J.F. Sipp & Associates) was there at the beginning and helped me to understand health insurance. Beth B. Parrott (Owner, Parrott Insurance and Benefits) shared her perspective and helpful advice. Robert S. Hurley (Senior Vice-president of Carrier Relations, eHealth Inc.) gave me some great perspective on a national scale from his position at one of the largest agencies in the country. Teresa Penninger (Individual Benefits Specialist, Parrott Insurance and Benefits) helped me to visualize the different types of people who are coming in to buy their own health insurance. Marge Schiller (CFP, NAPFA Registered Financial Advisor, Goar, Endriss, and Walker, P.A.) was kind enough to distill her vast knowledge about personal finance and health insurance into a single, powerful paragraph. Thanks to Sande Drew at eHealth for making things happen, Katherine Farless for bringing people together, and the Harrington Bank team for letting me take pictures of stacks of money. A big thanks to my designers, who have helped to make this book look great: John Labovitz and Heather Herndon. Thanks to my team of readers who helped me to make this the best health insurance book: John Labovitz, Nanette Efird, Larry and Leesa O'Neal, Yolanda and Hank Bravo, Karen DePaola, and my wonderful wife Victoria. Thanks to my family, who has been very supportive during this effort: Victoria, Madeleine, Harrison, Charlie, Linda, Chester, and Annie-Annie.

I also want to acknowledge the major contribution of those who have written on health insurance: authors, journalists, government employees, professors, business-people, association employees, insurance professionals, financial planners, and on and on. Since I'm a parent, I always talk in cliches, so here goes: "I am standing on the shoulders of giants."

For the latest updates, additional information, online tools, and more, go to:

www.BestHealthInsuranceBook.com

Chapter 1

How to Get a Good Deal

Do you like to get the most for your money? Have you thought about whether you are getting the best deal on health insurance? I had not when at my last employer because health insurance was paid for entirely by the employer. But when I left and paid to continue my insurance, I figured that I was probably getting a good deal: I was part of a group policy with lots of coverage that I thought would cost less than buying my own insurance.

Boy, was I wrong! It took a lot of time to gather all the information in this book, and I made mistakes along the way, but in the end I've selected a quality insurer, found a policy that works for my family, and I'm paying a whole lot less each month.

My monthly payment for benefits from my previous employer was $1,166 a month and included dental and vision. My payment after using the comparison method presented in this book is $296 a month. It started at $318 a month when I began the book, but I made changes as I learned more. I chose to skip the dental and vision coverage. That's a savings of $870 a month, or $10,440 a year. I feel good about the coverage that I'm getting, along with the other choices I've made in terms of benefit levels. I can honestly say that I sleep well at night with the coverage we've got.

> My health insurance payment started at $1,166 a month on COBRA, and went to $318 a month when I started this book. I made changes as I learned more and my monthly payment went to $296 a month, with a better plan!

Reading about health insurance is not at the top of my list of fun things to do, and reading the source materials on the topic has helped me to fall asleep on many occasions. In this book I'll try to keep it light and interesting, hitting the important points. The appendices and the website www.BestHealthInsuranceBook.com list additional resources for those who wish to go deeper.

I did not set out to write a book about health insurance. I was working on a different book which included a chapter about how to get your own health insur-

> "Health insurance is very personal: you're dealing with emotions, not just cost."
> -Beth B. Parrott, Owner, Parrott Insurance and Benefits

ance. Once I dug in and started my research, I found that there was much more material than could fit in one chapter. While some of the material can be found elsewhere, there is some very unique information that can only be found here: which includes a technique to compare all health plans "apples to apples," how to avoid being ripped-off, and a simple yet comprehensive way to view all of the health plan information.

In the past, I have used health insurance provided by an employer. When leaving employment or working somewhere with no benefits, I've used the continuation benefits from a job that I or my wife was working at when one of us left. I have purchased individual insurance from private insurers without really knowing what options I had or how well the plan I bought would work for me. I've also been ripped-off: in subtle ways and in some very big ways, and I hope that you can avoid some of the traps that have gotten me.

In this guide, you will learn how to get the best deal on health insurance – *for you*. Not a good deal for someone else, but a technique that will provide you with a comparison of how well each of your available health insurance options meets your needs, and how much your total health expenditures can be – whether in a good year, or a year where there are one or more health emergencies in your household.

What is a Good Deal?

Before launching into the process of getting a good deal, you should briefly review the factors that constitute a good deal. Each of the following points in Figure 1.1 is an important factor in defining a good deal on health insurance.

What Makes a Good Deal?
1. Value: Getting the most for your money.
2. Necessity: Paying for only what you need and not pricey extras that do not help you or that you don't use.
3. No Gaps: Making sure that you are getting the coverage that you need without any costly gaps, especially if you are unaware of them.
4. Long Term: Ensuring that short-term savings don't mean long-term (future) higher expenses and financial hardship.
5. As Promised: Ensuring that you actually get that which you are paying for, and don't get the run-around when trying to use the benefits.
6. Easy to Use: Minimizing the amount of work and hassle involved in the purchase, maintenance, and use of the plan.

Figure 1.1: What Makes a Good Deal?

Let's explore getting the most for your money in more detail.

1. Value

Getting the most for your money means getting the best value for you. This may not be the same value as your sister, your best friend, or your neighbor. For example, two different people drive cars – one sees the best value in getting the most miles to a gallon of gas. Another sees getting the most enjoyment from a gallon of gas. While the first may be trying to save money, the second may be trying to enjoy the act of driving, placing that at a higher priority than the additional cost of fuel. Both are trying to get the most for their money, but they are after different goals. This is true of health insurance, where different coverages and approaches will be better for different people – not a one-size-fits-all approach. Some people are more attracted to having a lower monthly payment, others are more attracted to having a lower deductible.

2. Necessity

Each and every feature that is included in a health insurance plan has a cost. Many plans are combinations of features that are offered together as an attractive package. Few allow à la carte choice in features, allowing you to configure your own coverage. Having additional features may be nice, but if you never use them, then you are paying money for nothing.

You can look at this like the way different automotive manufacturers sell cars. The first manufacturer offers many different options that you could add on separately if you desired.

It takes a lot more time to go through all the options you could add on, but this process also ensures that you buy only what you need, assuming you do not get tempted by all the cool accessories. Another manufacturer's purchasing process offers a few packages that group many options together. This process is a lot simpler and less time-consuming for a buyer. However, you end up paying for an option that is part of a group whether you need it or not. It can be the same with health insurance policies that group features together. For health insurance, however, you may end up paying for an unnecessary feature over and over every month and every year that you have the unused feature, which, as you might imagine, can be extremely costly.

3. No Gaps

Gaps are health insurance needs that are not paid by your plan. For example,

> ☼ "I review insurance coverages with everybody."
> -Lauren Gadkowski Lindsay, CFP®, NAPFA Registered Financial Advisor, Personal Financial Advisors

having a limited number of days in the hospital for an illness may mean that the plan stops paying after you've been in the hospital for a maximum number of days, for example, Medicare's 150 day hospital maximum. It is also possible that your insurance will only pay up to a certain amount, the daily maximum, and you pay the rest. An example of this is a health insurance policy with a hospital room and board maximum of $300 in an area where hospital charges always exceed this amount.

It is hard to know where the gaps are in any insurance plan. They all have some gaps, some are small and some are large. Reading the sales material before applying for health insurance doesn't answer many questions about gaps. Even reading the material that comes with any purchase may not clearly answer what is and is not covered because these decisions are made and revised over time, sometimes getting broader in what is covered, sometimes narrower. Your best bet to avoid encountering price gaps is to choose a plan offered by an insurer who is concerned about quality. You will see how to refine your search for health insurance for factors like quality in Chapter 7, and to avoid rip-offs in Chapter 10.

4. Long Term

A cheaper monthly payment may be attractive now, but if it means that in the future you will have big expenses because of what is and is not covered, then it is not a good deal. There are plans out there that cover what you need now for prevention and don't run out when you need them most in the future if something bad happens. Examples of plans that may lead to future hardships include a plan that offers a low annual maximum of $100,000 that would not likely pay enough in a year to cover an extremely serious medical problem. Or a low lifetime maximum ($500,000 to $1 Million) that might stop paying twenty years down the road after you've had a serious ongoing medical condition for many years and inflation has more than quadrupled the current costs of treatment.

5. As Promised

You are buying a plan that is supposed to pay for what it says, but sometimes you don't get what you pay for. It's important to choose a plan from a company that values quality and pays claims promptly and fully. You can ensure this by buying from a company of quality and checking out the complaints against any particular insurer with your state. Chapter 7 covers evaluating the quality of the insurance companies and the complaints against the companies.

6. Easy to Use

A good deal means that you don't have to continually file paperwork, deal with claim rejections and inquiries, and pay for medical expenses with little hope that you'll get reimbursed – often getting paid late if at all.

All of the factors involved in a good deal must be considered – both what you get as well as how much it costs. Remember, it's the best deal for you, not someone else.

Why You Need Health Insurance

For some people there is no question about it: you must have health insurance. When casually asking my friends, who are unhappy at their jobs, why they stay, the number one response is that they are staying in order to keep the health insurance – even though they and their families are healthy. For others, they may want health insurance but feel that it is always out of their grasp financially.

Over the years, I have known people who take the risk and do not get health insurance, simply because of the cost of individual health insurance plans. For example, young, single people just starting out, working for a small company, would rather pay for the one visit to the doctor out of pocket or simply not go to the doctor at all and don't buy insurance. Middle-income families in community rating states, where the minimum premium for health insurance is higher than other states, cannot afford the premium. Older folks who are self employed or contract workers, and therefore not eligible for group health plans, cannot afford health insurance on their own and take the risk that their health will be okay until Medicare kicks in, or stay tied to the job that provides their health insurance.

> "I do this exercise with my clients where I give them a list of values and I ask them to rank, in order, their top 5 values. One of them is health. Health is one of those in the top 5. I have people who do it every year and health moves up the list. As they get older the only thing they can't buy is their health. If you talk to older folks, health is so important, but when you're young it doesn't seem like the most important thing. I've seen enough health issues to value what I have. People don't make it a financial priority the way they need to. You only get one body and if you don't take care of it you're not going to get another one and you've got to live with it for the rest of your life."
> -Lauren Gadkowski Lindsay, CFP®, NAPFA Registered Financial Advisor, Personal Financial Advisors

There are many different stories of people who do not have health insurance and their reasons why. Whether to purchase health insurance and the cost of it is a major topic of discussion throughout the United States. Figure 1.2 lists the biggest risks of not having health insurance, some less obvious than others.

Biggest Risks of Not Having Health Insurance

1. Illness could bring a financial drain or financial ruin to you. Personal bankruptcy is frequently a consequence of a medical problem – and lack of insurance or lack of enough insurance can be part of the problem.
2. If you change your mind, you may not even be able to get coverage.
3. According to the Institute of Medicine, by skipping care when a condition is more treatable you have a statistically higher risk of dying when you don't have health insurance.
4. Skipping preventative care because of cost fears may lead to serious and expensive problems.

Figure 1.2: Biggest Risks of Not Having Health Insurance

Think about whether your parents, grandparents, or great-grandparents had health insurance. I can't remember my grandparents having health insurance. It wasn't that they were too poor to have it, although they might have been. It is more likely that health insurance was not widely available. Yet they managed to live well and live long. They didn't have any major health

> Massachusetts has a penalty on individual income tax if you don't have health insurance, or don't have enough. It is in the $200 dollar range this year.

episodes that broke the bank except at the end of their lives. I don't know that they ran out of money, as much as their bodies didn't last. Medicine can't cure everything, especially when dealing with some less than optimal life habits that can reduce health, like smoking, eating fatty/cholesterol laden foods, and not getting enough exercise.

As a parent with young children, I buy health insurance, as I might reasonably be expected to do. I have three children in school right now, and they are always in need of a little something here or there as strep throat, flu, and other maladies are passed from one child to the next. The wellness visits (annual checkups) are also important for everyone in the family – as we believe more in prevention than correction after the fact.

> "Are you looking for insurance to cover you in a catastrophic situation so you don't have to sell your house and everything you own, or do you think you'll be taking the kids frequently enough that copay options might be viable?"
> -Dianne Lawton, Former Director of Individual Sales, John F. Sipp & Associates

If you don't have health insurance in this country and need medical attention, the doctor will expect you to pay a much higher rate than they've negotiated with the major insurers. While this is unfair for customers paying cash, it is due to the leverage that the insurers use to negotiate the rates down for their benefit. Since the individual does not have much leverage, and is less likely to pay the bill, you can see why doctors' offices do this. If you want to negotiate the fees, you'll have to do that with the office manager in advance of the appointment – if they'll even negotiate – and continue to negotiate with everyone in the healthcare chain, including labs, hospitals, pharmacies, and so on. If you try this route, you'll want to keep track of all your negotiations in writing.

Would you expect to have a major operation if something went wrong, or have other extreme measures to save your life? If so, then you will want some level of insurance. These heroic procedures that can save your life and prolong it can also bankrupt you if you don't have some level of catastrophic insurance. But if you're in reasonably good shape, lead a healthy life, and don't have a family history of major disease that is not preventable, you might briefly consider the possibility of doing without insurance, although I wouldn't – I don't like to live that dangerously. You may be eligible for Medicare when you reach the current eligibility age of 65, and the hospitalization (Medicare Part A) might not even cost you anything if you've worked the equivalent of ten full-time years, though you'll need to pay

> **Percent of Uninsured Individuals, by Age**
> *from U.S. Census Bureau Statistics*

Age Range	Percent Uninsured
Under 18 years	11.2%
18 to 24 years	30.6%
25 to 34 years	26.4%
35 to 44 years	18.8%
45 to 64 years	14.6%
65 years and older	1.3%

for the doctors office and prescription portions of Medicare yourself, and get a Medigap policy to further reduce your risk. The fears of the cost of insurance is enough to keep many chained to their workplace until regular retirement age.

One health insurance agent told me that he thought because I kept the COBRA coverage from my previous employer (the option to keep health insurance from an employer where you pay the full amount that the employer pays) for so long was because we had health problems. Most folks only keep it for a few months until they find something else, unless they have a medical condition that would prevent getting individual coverage.

One of the most difficult things to overcome when purchasing health insurance is a pre-existing medical condition. It also happens to be one of the most popular reasons why some people fear being unemployed, because they or a dependent have a pre-existing condition that would limit their available health insurance options. You'll find more information about pre-existing conditions and coverage for those with a medical condition in Chapters 2, 6, 9, and 10.

Annual Health Insurance Cost Increases

You've heard it in the news – health insurance costs are skyrocketing. However, health insurance costs are not the same in each part of the country, in each state, or even in each ZIP code. The most recent data shows that the sharp increases are gone,

> ⚙ "Most media talks about group sponsored health insurance, which can be quite expensive."
> -Bob Hurley, Senior Vice President of Carrier Relations, eHealthInsurance.com

with a slower growth rate now. The increases also differ among insurers, and among types of plans offered by the insurer. Your age, always going up, is another factor in the increasing costs, one that is not reflected in any survey on health insurance inflation. The chances of needing medical care drop drastically after the first few years of life, creep up once we near middle age, and finally shoot up in the last years of life.

To get an idea of how much the health insurance premiums go up each year, let's look at some statistics from organizations that study these markets. The Kaiser Family Foundation, and the Health Research and Educational Trust, both independent non-profit groups with a mission to provide healthcare information, publish an annual survey entitled "Employer Health Benefits." This is an annual survey of the trends of purchasing group plans by employers. This is not exactly the same as an individual buying insurance, but it gives some idea about the upward nature of rates for both types of insurance.

This study has shown double digit increases in the first few years of the new century, as high as 13.9% in 2003. However, the trend is currently downward, with a 7.7% increase in 2006. But this downward trend is still more than twice the overall inflation rate, and the overall increase since 2000 for family coverage has been 87%.

With this in mind, it is important to monitor your health insurance coverage and consider new options as they become available to you. Once you've gone through the process presented in this book, you can easily update

> ⚙ "If we could equalize the tax treatment for everyone, I believe a sizable number would buy their own health insurance coverage, from outside, free from the chain to their employer. We give ourselves the portability to move about, changing employers and states. We want independence. People say that they would rather have their employers load up their paycheck and they'll go find the best health insurance"
> -Bob Hurley, Senior Vice President of Carrier Relations, eHealthInsurance.com

your options with new insurers and new plans on an annual basis – and switch if something makes better sense for you.

Your Health Insurance Annual Checkup

Just like your body, your health plan also needs an annual checkup. You have to investigate and manage your health plan on an ongoing basis – not just once. Particular times to check:

- After you get a rate increase.
- After you change age (usually in 5 year bracket – 40, 45, 50, etc.).
- When you add or remove dependents.
- When your health changes (for the better or worse).

Although managing your own health plan may seem like a lot of work, it does allow you the flexibility to buy and pay for only what you need. It ultimately gives you control over how you spend your money with regards to your health. For example, you can change plans when you need to, you can cover family members individually, and you can take advantage of the constantly changing health insurance plans available to cut your costs.

Unlike an employer's group plan, in many cases as an individual you can change coverage or insurers anytime in a year. This means you have control over how you are covered – and as new products come out on the health insurance market, you can be first in line to buy them.

You can insure different people in your household on different policies for different coverage or rates. Sometimes it doesn't make sense to put everyone on the same plan such as when one family member's health is poor, but the rest of the household is healthy. Instead of lumping everyone into a higher-premium plan, shopping around for coverage separately in addition to investigating health insurance for the entire household may save you significant money over the course of a year.

> You can mix and match insurance policies for different household members. For example, put the healthiest on one policy and those with a medical condition each on their own separate policy.

New companies, products, and approaches are appearing to satisfy the new needs and desires of those buying health insurance. If you aren't thrilled with the options available, keep shopping and new options will open up. For example, when I first left my job I went with the COBRA option, and checked with that insurer for any individual policies. There weren't any. But as I am doing this research, well over a year later, it is possible to obtain insurance through this company – as part of an association. This makes it a very appealing option, since the network, doctors, and policies appear to be very similar between the plan available through COBRA and through the association plan. You'll want to read Chapter 6 about association insurance and whether it's the right choice for you.

If you find yourself traveling to different locations, whether frequently or for short or long periods of time, make sure that you investigate plans that provide you and your dependents with coverage where you go. Some HMO/PPO plans have nationwide networks, some have only local networks. With some it doesn't matter who you see (traditional indemnity insurance), and coverage outside of the U.S. varies, with a majority of plans not covering anything but an emergency. Additional international policies may be found, you could self-insure for trips, or you could look into short-term health coverage at your destination when traveling outside your main plan area.

Check into the available healthcare in the places that you will frequent. If you spend most of your time at home, but have a national network in a PPO, you'll be able to get covered healthcare when you are away from home on travel. If you travel internationally, you can either use a plan with built-in international coverage, or get a short term international policy.

If you move to a different part of the state, or to a different state, then you may not be able to keep your current health insurance coverage. If you have any significant medical condition, it may make sense to reconsider a move, or at least maintain residency in the location of your current health plan to avoid major increases in premiums when shopping for a new plan, or outright denial of coverage. The place to start for your annual health insurance checkup is with your agent, web sites in this book, and www.BestHealthInsuranceBook.com.

Steps to Get the Best Deal

In this chapter, you have read about the basis of a good deal, why you need health insurance, the annual cost increases of health insurance premiums, and why you need an annual checkup on your health insurance. The rest of the book consists of the process to follow in order to get a good deal on health insurance, along with resources and tips on avoiding rip-offs.

The steps to get the best deal are presented in Figure 1.3. Read through the overview of the steps to get an idea of what is involved. Each of the chapters that follows includes one or more of these steps, as well as tips, diagrams, and other resources. There are also more resources available at our website, www.BestHealthInsuranceBook.com.

Steps to Get the Best Deal

1. Learn and understand health insurance. (Chapter 2)
2. Determine options on where to get it – at work, etc. (Chapter 3)
3. Determine features important to you. (Chapter 4)
4. Estimate your anticipated annual expenses. (Chapter 5)
5. Decide if you should pursue group or individual. (Chapter 6)
6. Obtain a list of insurers for your state. (Chapter 7)
7. Edit your list of insurers. (Chapter 7)
8. Get quotes from each insurer or source. (Chapter 8)
9. Compare quotes. (Chapter 8)
10. Choose your best deal. (Chapter 9)
11. Apply for insurance. (Chapter 9)
12. Cancel existing insurance. (Chapter 9)
13. Avoid Rip-Offs! (Chapter 10)

Figure 1.3: Steps to Get the Best Deal

Overview of Chapters

The remainder of this book is presented in a chronological order of the steps to get the best deal when purchasing your own health insurance. Each of the chapters are listed and briefly summarized below. Depending on your own personal preference or need you can either start at the beginning and read through the chapters as presented, or if you already have some knowledge regarding purchasing health insurance or have a particular question, read the chapters that pertain to you directly. I suggest that you read through once to become familiar with the entire process and then return to each chapter as you go through the health insurance purchasing process, with pen and paper in hand as you gather your information.

Sometimes it seems that the alphabet soup of insurance terms and abbreviations are only intended to intimidate you. In Chapter 2, you'll get a quick review of the most important terms and some graphics to help illustrate the meaning of the terms for the "picture people". Chapter 3 tells you the many places that you can get health insurance – and some of the characteristics of each place to get health insurance. Chapter 4 provides more terms related to the various features that you may encounter in plans while shopping, along with a way to keep track of features important to you.

Predicting your health expenditures is not an exact science, but it can be helpful to get an idea of what you've spent and then project that into the future, as explained in Chapter 5. Chapter 6 helps you to understand different types of health insurance – including individual or group, with comparisons between the various types.

> ### ⚕ Five Ways to Save Money on Health Insurance
> 1. Be at your healthiest. If you weren't when joining, find out if you can reduce your premium by quitting smoking, losing weight, and exercising regularly.
> 2. Increase your deductible - Just like automobile and homeowners insurance, the rate goes down when the deductible goes up.
> 3. Remove unnecessary coverages. Drop things like vision and dental if you are not making use of them regularly.
> 4. Increase your copay. Changing from a $10 to a $20, $30, or $40 copay will bring down your premium.
> 5. Switch from a copay plan to one without. With copays the insurer is taking more risk. If you are willing to drop the copay and pay the office visit amount yourself (currently about $55 for the negotiated discount in my area), you can save money if you don't visit the doctor frequently.

Chapter 7 helps you to obtain the list of authorized insurers from your state and leads you through the process of narrowing down these insurers. Once you have the short list of insurers that meet your criteria, you can proceed to accumulate quotes and options from these insurers, as detailed in Chapter 8. This is where the most legwork is involved, as you gather information from each company, either directly from an insurer or through an agent. This chapter also shows a mathematical way to compare all the numbers provided – and a way for you to determine which company and plans to pursue further. After helping you to make a decision, Chapter 9 explains the process of applying for new insurance, and the steps that follow.

Chapter 10 provides tips to keep you from becoming the victim of the many rip-offs that exist in the health insurance marketplace. The appendices provide contact information and internet addresses for resources that you'll need as you work through the steps in this book.

You'll also want to keep up-to-date with additional information along with downloads and online tools from the website, www.BestHealthInsuranceBook.com.

Chapter 2

Understanding Health Insurance Jargon

In this chapter we'll focus on piles of money: stacks of dollar bills, and the different health insurance terms to which they correspond, with the goal of helping you to understand how you can keep as much money in your pocket as possible.

If you want to hang on to your hard earned dollars, you have to understand key health insurance terms as well as or better than the insurance companies. Health insurance has its own specific set of jargon. You have probably heard all the terms before, but may have had a hard time fully understanding them. There are so many terms, and some are more important than others when you are buying health insurance. If you're not involved with health insurance in some professional capacity, these terms can be confusing and unnerving when you are forced to confront them at a time when you need to buy your own health insurance. However, you need to fully understand the jargon when you undertake the task of comparing offerings from different insurers. You will need to look at the major terms together, not just one, to determine which plan gives you a good deal on health insurance. You won't just compare copays to find the lowest copay, or deductibles to find the lowest deductible, without looking at the other parts of the plan.

> "We spend a lot of time with our clients explaining health insurance so that they understand it."
> -Jennifer McLaurin, Director of Sales, John F. Sipp & Associates

Many of the explanations available elsewhere consist of what amounts to dictionary definitions, and I encourage you to read them. Instead of repeating those definitions here, you'll learn the terms through the use of a diagram that shows how most of the terms relate to each other, as well as a brief explanation of the terms from the perspective of how they contribute to getting a good deal. In addition, the diagram will be presented several times for different types of plans towards the end of the chapter, so that you can readily see by example how to differentiate between what the terms mean in these general types of plans.

> On my first visit to the health insurance agents' office, I was asked what level of deductible I'd be comfortable with. I didn't understand how important this question was - and how much it has to do with the rate you'll get.

You can also go to the website at www.BestHealthInsuranceBook.com to use online tools that will generate diagrams and help you to figure out your best deal.

The most important terms to getting a good deal are listed in Figure 2.1. These terms will all be discussed in this chapter, and many of them will appear in diagrams to help understand their interrelationships.

The Most Important Health Insurance Terms for a Good Deal

1. Copay (or Copayment)
2. Deductible
3. Coinsurance
4. Total Out of Pocket
5. Lifetime Limit/Annual Limit
6. Health Maintenance Organization (HMO)
7. Preferred Provider Organization (PPO)
8. Point of Service (POS)
9. Indemnity (Major Medical) Health Insurance
10. Health Savings Account (HSA)
11. High Deductible Health Plan (HDHP)
12. Underwriting
13. Medical Condition
14. Community Rating
15. Exclusionary Riders
16. Pre-Existing Condition
17. Waiting Period
18. Eligible Expenses

Figure 2.1: The Most Important Health Insurance Terms for a Good Deal.

Referring to Figure 2.2 you'll see two stacks of dollar bills. The stack on the left is for the "big dollar" benefits and the stack on the right is for the "little dollar" benefits, primarily those covered by copays.

Figure 2.2: Big Dollar Versus Little Dollar

Many of the essential health insurance terms are presented in Figure 2.3. You can see how they are interrelated through the placement in the diagram. The terms are discussed in further detail following the diagram overview, and specific examples are presented towards the end of the chapter.

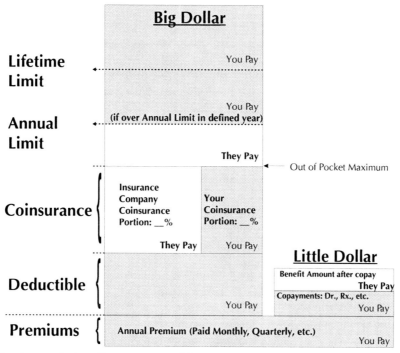

Figure 2.3: The Interrelation Between Health Insurance Terms.

Here's how the "dollar bills" stack up in Figure 2.3. Starting at the bottom, below "ground level", you pay all the insurance premiums (the premium is the amount you pay monthly to the insurance company). The reason that the diagram has premiums below "ground level" is because many term definitions do not include the premiums that you pay. However, you are paying them, and they can vary greatly between plans from different insurers and from the same insurer. The financial comparison provided in Chapter 8 takes the premium into account. However, for the purposes of understanding the terms, the premiums are not taken into account. Incredibly, they are not counted by the insurers in the definition of "total out of pocket" even though the money is coming out of your pocket!

Then starting at ground level, there are two unrelated money stacks – the one on the right ("little dollar") shows the copays that you make, which can range from anywhere from zero to ten, twenty, thirty, or more dollars per occurrence or use of the benefit (e.g. a trip to the doctors office). The rest of the cost of the services are paid by the insurance company, which is shown in the box for benefits that is above the copays. It is important to note that the copays, and of course the benefits paid by the insurer, do not count towards the deductible in the stack on the left.

The stack on the left ("big dollar") shows the deductible for which you are fully responsible for covering before any insurance benefits kick in, with the exception of copay and wellness types of benefits. Once the deductible has been met with eligible expenses, then the amount that you pay will be reduced by a percentage in the coinsurance, the split between what you pay and the insurance company pays up to a fixed dollar amount. Once the coinsurance maximum is met, then the plan pays 100% of expenses, up to an annual maximum on some plans, and a lifetime maximum on others.

Copay (or Copayment)

Some plans, typically the managed care plans like HMO and PPO (discussed later in this chapter), offer a "copay" option. Essentially you have a fixed price for a doctor visit, a specialist visit, a prescription, or a laboratory test. Not all plans offer copays for all services, and some have different copay amounts for the different types of services, such as a regular doctor (like a general practitioner) visit or a specialist (like a dermatologist) visit. A copay can also apply to a prescription as well as any other service that an insurance plan offers. The amount can range from zero dollars, typically for wellness visits on some plans, to ten, twenty, thirty, or more dollars per doctor visit, prescription, laboratory service, or other plan feature.

The copay is one of the widely known and understood words used for health insurance. You go to the doctor, you pay a fixed amount. Simple. Keep in mind, though, that a lower copay does not mean a lower cost plan (it's usually a higher cost plan), or necessarily a better deal. It may make financial sense if you see yourself visiting the doctor very frequently. It also makes it psychologically easier to access healthcare if a doctor visit is ten or twenty dollars, versus forty dollars in a higher copay plan. It's also easier to think about a fixed amount, rather than to pay for a doctor visit in full. But a higher copay, or absence of a copay, may mean a significantly lower monthly premium rate – and the doctor visit may still cost you less than paying month after month, year after year, for a copayment option.

> A lower copay usually means a higher premium. It may not give you the best deal if you don't frequent the doctor's office – since you will pay for visits that you may not make.

Some plans have prescription copays for different types of prescriptions – generic, preferred, and name brand. A higher copay may reduce your monthly rate, but if you are making frequent doctor visits, as you might with young children, then it makes sense to compare all the features of a plan as explained in Chapter 4. Before you start comparing plans try to estimate how many doctor visits you would typically make in a given year (based on the total number of doctor visits in previous years) which is discussed in further detail in Chapter 5.

Having a copayment as part of a plan may mean that you pay a higher premium than for a comparable plan that does not pay until you have satisfied the deductible.

Deductible

The deductible is the expense that you pay for health services that are eligible expenses before your health insurance policy begins paying. This does not apply to items with a copay. So for a plan that has a copay, the $20 that you spend to see your doctor does not count towards the deductible, but expenses paid while in the hospital would. You will begin paying towards the deductible immediately until you've reached the deductible maximum. Some policies have a maximum per individual as well as per couple or per family, so understanding this number is impor-

> Generally, the higher the deductible amount, the lower your monthly premium. But if something goes wrong with your health, you'll need the money that you saved by taking lower premiums, so don't spend it on anything else: invest it.

tant. It is also important to know for which expenses you only have to pay a copay and which ones you pay in full with the amount going towards the deductible.

Don't be easily scared off by a plan with a high deductible. We have gone many years without incurring a medical expense that was applied toward the deductible. Over the years, we've had plans with a copay option that have paid for all of the expenses that we incurred. When you visit a health insurance agent, you will be asked what kind of deductible you are comfortable with. After reviewing the information in this book, you may find that you are more comfortable with a larger deductible, knowing that you may be able to build up a financial emergency fund with money saved in premiums within the first years of a policy and also knowing that you may not incur an expense that isn't covered by a copay. You may find that such a plan may actually be less expensive in the long run, and save you money. Then again, you might feel that a low copay and deductible are right for you – from a plan that may have a higher premium.

Coinsurance

Coinsurance is the expense that you will split with the insurance company before the insurance company pays in full for eligible expenses. It is usually expressed as a percentage and a dollar amount. Typically coinsurance starts after you have satisfied an individual or family deductible and continues until you've reached the coinsurance maximum amount. Sometimes the coinsurance percentage is expressed as the amount that you will pay, and sometimes as the amount the insurance company will pay, making it even more confusing.

You need to look at the percentage and the amount together. For example, if you had medical bills of $8,000, a 50% coinsurance amount with a limit of $8,000 will result in $4,000 in payments by you after you've satisfied your deductible and a $4,000 payment by the insurance company. An 80% coinsurance amount on a limit of $10,000 will result in a maximum of $2,000 in payments by you after you've satisfied your deductible, with the insurance company paying $8,000 of the expenses before paying entirely for any other eligible expenses.

Coinsurance is paid on a dollar-by-dollar basis, with you paying your share (percent) of each dollar, and the insurance company paying their share (percent) of each dollar. To better understand this, consider an example. Let's say you have health insurance with a $1,000 deductible and a 50% coinsurance on the next $10,000. If you have medical bills of $5,000 then you pay the first $1,000 as the deductible. The remaining $4,000 of the bill is subject to coinsurance. With a 50/50 split, you are responsible for $2,000 and the insurance company for $2,000. If you had an 80/20 split on the coinsurance, you'd be responsible for $800, with the insurance company paying $3,200.

Having coinsurance can reduce your expenses during a medical event, but can also raise the premium that you pay month after month, year after year. The increased premiums may amount to a difference of thousands of dollars over time as compared to a plan with no coinsurance and the same deductible.

Make sure that there is an upper limit to the amount of coinsurance that you might pay, otherwise you could be responsible for your percent of a very large medical bill – and unable to afford it. For example, if you required a $500,000 medical procedure, and you were only covered for 80%, then you would be responsible for $100,000!

Total Out of Pocket

The total out of pocket is the deductible amount plus the share of coinsurance that you pay. For example, an individual plan with a $5,000 deductible and a 50% coinsurance on the next $5,000 will give you a total out of pocket amount of $7,500. However, the total out of pocket is a misnomer because it does not include amounts spent on premiums, copays, or prescriptions. It is simply the "big dollar" amounts of how much you will have to pay if something medically significant happens.

The total out of pocket can be expressed on an individual basis or on a family basis. The family out of pocket is the individual out of pocket maximum multiplied by a number, which can be less than the total number of family members. I've seen family out of pocket maximums that are one, two, or three times the individual out of pocket maximums. For example, a family policy with a $5,000 deductible, a 50% coinsurance on the next $5,000, and a two person family maximum, will have a total out of pocket of $15,000 ($5,000 x 2 + $2,500 x 2), regardless if there are more family members on the plan.

Looking at total out of pocket is one way to compare apples-to-apples when you have health insurance quotes from different companies. Comparing a plan with similar attributes, but a different number of family members required to meet the limit, can result in some significant differences in the money that you may have to come up with if you or a family member experiences a medical problem.

Lifetime Limit/Annual Limit

The lifetime limit is a maximum that the company or policy will pay during your lifetime of coverage. These range from the low millions of dollars (e.g., one million, five million) to unlimited. The annual limit is the maximum amount that will be paid in benefits during the year. Keep in mind that depending on the policy, the year could be a calendar year or any 12-month period.

If you are in the position that you or a household member requires significant healthcare, such as a transplant, an annual limit of $100,000 may not be enough considering that few transplants can be done for less than this amount (and check any plan to see if transplants are even covered). Having a lifetime limit of only a million dollars could mean that health benefits might run out when you really need them in the future, as prices go up.

Having an annual limit or a low lifetime limit may reduce your premiums, but it may not be worth the savings. The biggest reason to have the health insurance is to manage expenses that you might not be able to pay yourself. If your coverage runs out when you really need it – after a major medical problem – how will you feel?

Health Maintenance Organization (HMO)

A Health Maintenance Organization (HMO) is a health plan that offers services through a list of specific providers, sometimes employees of a HMO owned facility, sometimes through contracted doctors and facilities. HMO plans typically have a list of contracted doctors, hospitals, and facilities (commonly known as the network) whose expenses will be covered by the plan. Because you are

> HMO plans have a reputation of being the cheapest, but since they are frequently full of features, non-HMO plans that offer fewer features can have a lower premium.

limited to using their contracted doctors and facilities, plans in this category have lower costs in this area but HMO plans tend to be full featured, and there are more limited plans based on the PPO model that may cost less.

If you wish to see a doctor not contracted with the plan, the plan will not cover the visit, leaving you to pay for the medical expenses. In some cases, you must designate a primary physician and see that primary physician first for any medical care other than emergencies. The primary physician will then decide whether referrals to other doctors are necessary, taking on a role known as the gatekeeper, slowing down or denying access to specialists.

Preferred Provider Organization (PPO)

This option provides for more flexibility than an HMO. It may offer an HMO type of network and provide a higher level of coverage when using providers in the network, but it also provides coverage to providers outside of the network, though at a lower level of coverage, meaning that you will pay a larger amount of the bill. This keeps the option to use non-network providers, but also gives you the choice of using the network doctors at a lower cost. If your doctors and facilities are all in-network, then you might save money by using an HMO/POS over a PPO, but check out the available options, because like everything else in health insurance, it varies depending on the insurer and policy.

Point of Service (POS)

A variation on the HMO is the Point of Service (POS), which is also very much like a PPO, but offered as part of an HMO plan. Point of Service means that the type of coverage you will receive depends on the point (or place) of service. A POS plan provides a list of doctors and facilities that, if used, provides for more flexibility and a similar low-cost approach to healthcare as an HMO. Use of doctors and facilities outside of the HMO or network may not be covered in full as the charges from these providers are not pre-negotiated with the insurer. The difference here is that some part of the expenses/charges may be covered, sometimes up to the amount that the insurer deems "reasonable and customary," meaning the amount they would pay for the exact same procedure code to a doctor within the network, minus the percentage that you are responsible for paying when going out of network.

Indemnity Health Insurance

An Indemnity Health Insurance plan, also known as major medical, is a more flexible yet more costly option. Many people refer to this as a traditional plan because it preceded the advent of managed care: HMO, PPO, POS. You choose your doctors and facilities and then the insurer pays, subject to any deductibles or coinsurance. Some plans may offer wellness visits, such as an annual physical, but you may pay more for this benefit even though in the long term wellness would keep health expenses down. Because of the flexibility and control that you have over the delivery of the benefits, this can be an expensive option. You'll know if you need this type of insurance based on the available healthcare options in your area after researching the doctors that are in-network with the managed care plans available to you.

Managed Care Versus Indemnity

Managed care health plans, such as an HMO or PPO, may provide more benefits for the same or less money than an indemnity (major medical or traditional) plan because it uses an approved set of doctors and hospitals with whom it has negotiated lower rates. However, if you don't need all of the services provided by a managed care provider it is still possible that you may be able to get a better deal elsewhere by getting a plan that covers fewer costs. In general, however, you typically will be able to get a lower rate with a managed care provider. Some people use a managed care plan like an

> You may have heard about how procedures are denied by a medical administrator at a managed care insurer – but the same can be said of an indemnity insurer, with the difference that they might not pay after the fact, instead of denying the procedure up-front. Plus you still face limits of 'reasonable and customary' charges any time you are seeking care outside of a network.

indemnity plan, accepting the limitations of the network and administration, in order to get a better deal on their health insurance.

Health Savings Account & High Deductible Health Plan

A Health Savings Account (HSA) is not to be confused with the other "SA's" (MSA's, FSA's, HRA's, etc.). Unlike an HSA, the others can be advantageous for an employer/employee as a benefit, but generally cost money, have a use it or lose it policy, and are very limited in how much you can put into the account and what it can be spent on.

The HSA is an account much like an IRA into which you can deposit a limited amount of money without paying any federal income tax on that money. The added bonus is that the unused portion stays in the account year-after-year, accumulating tax-free interest. The money can be used for a wide variety of medical purposes including things not covered by most health insurers. Plus, when you hit 65, you can take money out for non-medical purposes just like an IRA: you pay income tax on the distributions. You can

> IRS Publication 969 explains HSA's and IRS Publication 502 lists many eligible expenses that insurance may not typically cover such as:
> - Acupuncture
> - Chiropractic
> - Contact Lenses/Supplies
> - Dental
> - Fertility
> - Guide Dog
> - Lodging during treatment
> - Long-Term Care Insurance
> - Medicines
> - Osteopathic

even get access to the money before 65 for non-medical purposes by paying a 10% penalty in addition to income tax.

Some states follow the federal approach and allow contributions to an HSA that are free of state income tax. The federal contribution can be a deduction from your tax return to the maximum contribution in 2008 of $2,900 for a single person or $5,800 for a family.

An HSA must be coupled with a High Deductible Health Plan (HDHP), which is likely to be similar to an indemnity or PPO policy with a higher deductible. An HDHP must be HSA qualified – some HDHP's don't have HSA as part of it, due to some part of the benefit package not qualifying. The HDHP must have a deductible within a certain range. The minimum and maximum deductible in 2008 for a single person is $1,100 and $5,600 and for a family is $2,200 and $11,200. Prior year limitations on contributions that were tied to the number of months that the policy is in effect were removed, which means that you can contribute the maximum regardless when you started the plan. Prior to the change, the amount was pro-rated for the months in a calendar that you had the plan.

HSA's are offered by lots of financial institutions. You can match your HDHP with an HSA from any institution, and the insurer probably offers one option bundled with the HDHP that you should consider. You can get different HSA features from different financial institutions, and can do searches for these accounts on the internet. You have the option of changing your HSA account provider separately from your health insurance provider. You can also change your HDHP account from one insurer to another and keep your HSA dollars. You can also switch from an HDHP to another type of health insurance and keep your HSA account, but you won't be able to contribute to it unless you have an HDHP.

An HSA/HDHP allows you to spend pre-tax dollars for your out-of-pocket health expenses using either a debit card or a checkbook from the HSA. However, with a few exceptions, this does not include health insurance premiums. You may save your HSA contributed dollars in the HSA and not spend them on healthcare during the year – a long term savings vehicle for healthcare expenses. You can then draw on these funds in the future for medical expenses, and when you reach age 65, you can use them as a retirement source of income the same way as an IRA, or for medical expenses, premiums, or to pay for long term care insurance. Like any program that involves the IRS, the complications of the HSA are numerous – so look before you leap. You may wish to find more information from the IRS or the numerous books on the topic. Look for internet resources at the website www.BestHealthInsuranceBook.com.

> ### ☼ HSA's are Evolving: Learn More on The Web
> - www.hsainsider.com bills itself as the leading destination on the internet.
> - www.hsafinder.com is run by a national speaker and author of two books on HSA's, who is the creator of the annual White House briefing on HSA's. "It is the leading independent website on health savings accounts, providing information about how to set-up an HSA, the latest regulations, how to make the most of your HSA and much more including insurance quotes for high-deductible health plans, comparative information on account custodians, and listings of support providers."
> -JoAnn M. Laing, Author, President & CEO, HSAFinder.com

Underwriting

Underwriting is the process that the insurance company uses to assess your application. During this process they will determine if you are insurable according to the company guidelines, finalize the rate that you will pay which could be greater or less than quoted, and determine if there are any special circumstances that will apply to you, such as excluding coverage for certain conditions.

Underwriting practices and formulas vary from company to company. They are part of the "trade secrets" of the insurance companies. However, a good agent will have some idea of the input criteria to the underwriting process, and help steer you towards the right company for you. Some states limit or do not allow a person's medical health to be used in underwriting, and these are generally the same states that have a community rating as described in the next section.

As an example see Figure 2.4. Underwriting guidelines for insurers in Texas were documented by the Texas government Office of Public Insurance Counsel. You can see how medical conditions, presented in the next section, and other factors contribute to denial of insurance, increases in rates, and decreases in coverage.

2007 Individual Health Insurance Underwriting Guidelines

UNDERWRITING GUIDELINE	USED TO DENY COVERAGE	USED TO CHARGE A HIGHER RATE	USED TO OFFER LESS COVERAGE	TOTAL PERCENT OF MARKET SURVEYED USING GUIDELINE FOR UNDERWRITING PURPOSES
MEDICAL CONDITION The company examines the medical history of each applicant, using questions on the application, follow-up phone calls, and a review of medical records. Applicants with certain medical conditions are considered uninsurable and are routinely denied coverage. Click here for a list of uninsurable diseases and conditions as compiled by the Texas Health Insurance Risk Pool. For many common health conditions, applicants may be accepted, denied, charged a higher rate, or offered less coverage. For a breakdown of the actions taken by the insurance companies for selected conditions, click here.	100%	100%	100%	100%
HEIGHT/WEIGHT The company increases premiums or deductibles based on Body Mass Index (BMI). Premium increases can be between 25-50% of the standard (acceptable) rate. If applicant's BMI is higher than 35, the company will reject the applicant According to the National Institutes of Health: 18.5 - 24.9 NORMAL 25.0 - 29.5 OVERWEIGHT 30.0 - 39.9 OBESE 40.0 and higher – MORBIDLY OBESE	100%	86%	14%	100%
MORALS/LIFESTYLE The company asks if the applicant has had any convictions including DWI/DUI, number of speeding tickets, and whether the applicant has used illegal substances/drugs or abused prescription medications. In most cases, if an applicant answers "yes", a further investigation is done, and most likely the applicant will be declined.	76%			76%
AVOCATIONS The company underwrites based on the hobbies of the applicant and considers whether the hobby is professional or amateur. Some examples include SCUBA, Sky Diving, Parachuting, and Rodeo.	52%	24%	48%	67%
INFORMATION FROM CONSUMER REPORTING AGENCIES The company must ask applicant for permission to obtain these reports.				
MEDICAL INFORMATION BUREAU (MIB) REPORT - These reports provide data that is collected by approximately 500 member insurance companies. Information on medical conditions, driving records, criminal activity, and participation in hazardous sports, and aviation activity is contained in these reports.	67%	67%	67%	67%
CREDIT REPORT – A record of an individual's past borrowing and repaying history, including information about late payments and bankruptcy	67%	67%	67%	67%

Figure 2.4: Individual Health Insurance Underwriting Guidelines – State of Texas

Produced by the Office of Public Insurance Counsel
www.opic.state.tx.us

2007 Individual Health Insurance Underwriting Guidelines

UNDERWRITING GUIDELINE	USED TO DENY COVERAGE	USED TO CHARGE A HIGHER RATE	USED TO OFFER LESS COVERAGE	TOTAL PERCENT OF MARKET SURVEYED USING GUIDELINE FOR UNDERWRITING PURPOSES
PRESCRIPTION DRUG HISTORY Each company has a separate list of declinable medications. Some examples include: regular insulin for diabetes treatment, Plavix for treatment of clots, and Aricept for Alzheimer's Disease. If a patient is currently taking medications on the unacceptable drug list, the company may decline the applicant. An insurer can also increase premiums or deductibles based on certain medication usage. Also, some insurers require the applicant to purchase endorsements excluding or limiting coverage.	52%	24%	24%	67%
RESIDENCY Some insurers require United States residency of 12–24 months before an applicant can apply for coverage. Other insurers will decline an applicant who is on Visa status.	67%			67%
OCCUPATION The insurer will have a list of occupations that will result in declining the applicant or will ask the applicant to purchase endorsements excluding or limiting coverage based on his/her occupation.	48%		19%	52%
REPUTATION The company asks an insurance agent and in some instances, conducts personal interviews with friends, neighbors, and associates, regarding the general reputation and characteristics of the applicant. A sample question for an agent is, "Are you aware of any information not disclosed on this application relating to the health, habits or reputation of any person listed on this application which might have a bearing on the risk?"	38%	38%	38%	38%
BLOOD TEST OR ATTENDING PHYSICIAN STATEMENT (APS)				
BLOOD TEST - In order to process an application, the company requires a blood test.	5%	5%	5%	5%
APS- In order to process an application, the company requires an Attending Physician Statement regarding the applicant's health. In most cases, this is the insured's physician.	33%	33%	33%	33%
DOMESTIC VIOLENCE The company underwrites impairments caused by domestic violence.	10%	10%	10%	10%

Produced by the Office of Public Insurance Counsel
www.opic.state.tx.us

29

Medical Condition

A medical condition is any one-time medical event that could have a lasting impact on health, as well as chronic conditions that require on-going medical treatments. Many times these will be used to deny insurance or increase rates during underwriting. If you develop one while on one policy and need to change policies, for example leaving a job with health insurance for one without, you must be careful how you proceed because having a serious medical condition could make you uninsurable once you leave an existing policy. A document prepared by the Texas Government Office of Public Insurance Counsel is presented in Figure 2.5, showing serious medical conditions that lead to application denials for individual and association group insurance.

UNINSURABLE MEDICAL CONDITIONS

Many health conditions are considered uninsurable due to the high cost of treatment and medications. When such conditions are listed on the application, many health insurance companies will decline coverage without further review of medical records. These conditions include but may not be limited to the following: [1]

---

[1] List of medical conditions taken from Texas Health Insurance Risk Pool Qualifying Medical/Health Conditions.

Cancer
  • Malignant Tumor within 4 Years (except skin cancer)
  • Metastatic
Cardiovascular
  • Artificial Heart Valve
  • Cardiomyopathy
  • Coronary Artery Disease
  • Polyarteritis Nodosa
  • Peripheral Vascular Disease
Endocrine/Exocrine
  • Diabetes Mellitus
  • Cystic Fibrosis
  • Addison's Disease
Gastrointestinal
  • Intestinal
    ○ Crohn's Disease
    ○ Ulcerative Colitis
  • Liver
    ○ Cirrhosis (non-alcoholic)
    ○ Wilson's Disease
    ○ Hepatitis
Hematopoietic
  • Anemia
    ○ Sickle Cell
    ○ Splenic (True Banti's Syndrome)
  • Hemophilia
  • Leukemia
  • Thalassemia
Hodgkin's Disease
Immunological
  • AIDS or HIV Positive
  • Lupus
	Musculoskeletal
	  • Dermatomyositis or Polymyositis
	  • Muscular Atrophy or Dystrophy
	  • Myotonia
	  • Rheumatoid Arthritis
	  • Still's Disease
	  • Legge-Perthes Disease
	Neurological - Central Nervous System
	  • Cerebral Palsy
	  • Cerebral Vascular Accident (CVA)
	  • Epilepsy
	  • Gullian-Barre Syndrome
	  • Huntington's Chorea
	  • Hydrocephalus
	  • Lead Poisoning with Cerebral Involvement
	  • Lobotomy
	  • Parkinson's Disease (if treatment within 3 years)
	Neurological - Periphal Nervous System
	  • Amyotrophic Lateral Sclerosis
	  • Friedrich's Ataxia
	  • Myasthenia Gravis
	  • Paraplegia or Quadriplegia
	  • Sclerosis, Multiple
	  • Syringomyelia
	  • Tabes Dorsalis (Locomotor Ataxia)
	Psychotic Disorders
	Pulmonary
	  • Silicosis (Black Lung)
	Renal
	  • Polycystic Kidney
	Other
	  • Brain Tumor
	  • Down's Syndrome
	  • Scleroderma
	  • Transplants

Produced by the Office of Public Insurance Counsel
www.opic.state.tx.us

Figure 2.5: Uninsurable Medical Conditions – State of Texas

Community Rating

Community rating is a way to charge everyone in a community the same amount of money in premiums, regardless of health conditions. Most of the states that have implemented this have some modifications that allow somewhat different rates based on the location in the state, number of family members, and few other criteria.

Community rating effectively levels the premium paid by all people in the state. The upside is that those who have a medical condition can find health insurance more affordably than without community rating. The downside is that healthier people are paying significantly higher premiums than in other states, in part because the state government requires many benefits to be mandatory. Unfortunately, the result is that people with financial resources are able to buy insurance, and many other people are priced out of the market, without other options available. Those who have financial resources and a medical condition are able to more affordably buy health insurance. However, those families without financial resources or without a medical condition may not be able to afford health insurance at all.

> States currently mandating community rating in purchase of individual insurance are:
> - Maine
> - Massachusetts
> - New York
> - New Jersey
> - Oregon
> - Vermont
> - Washington
> - Other states may offer community rating or guaranteed issue during certain times of year or with the state Blue Cross Blue Shield plan.

Many people who would be able to afford health insurance in other states are unable to do so in states that have community rating. This is important because people who are healthy and then encounter a medical condition while on an affordable insurance will continue to pay a reasonable rate. You shouldn't get re-underwritten once on a plan – you should only get underwritten when changing to a new plan. Without insurance, people are unable to afford or pay for care that they receive, and may end up in personal bankruptcy at a higher rate than those who have insurance to begin with.

When I lived in New Jersey, a community rating state, our family health insurance cost at least $850 a month, and that was a number of years ago. Living in North Carolina, similar feature rich plans cost hundreds less for a healthy family.

> Blue Cross Blue Shield of Rhode Island's individual plan allows the consumer to choose between community rating or medically underwritten rates. A great choice!

Exclusionary Riders

Exclusionary riders are additions to an insurance policy that exclude coverage for certain conditions. These can be for the life of the policy or for a stated period of time. Insurers can also adjust the premium amount because of these riders. Riders like these are not desirable, nor allowed in every state. However, rather than going without insurance, or being rejected for insurance, you may find that you can get a time limited exclusionary rider, for which you may then try to appeal for a time limit. You may also wish to appeal for a time limit on any exclusionary riders that may be proposed without any time limit. An experienced agent can tell you which companies have done this in the past, and help you to try.

Pre-Existing Condition

This is a medical condition that exists before the policy is in force. It may cause exclusionary riders, changes in the premium amounts, or waiting periods before coverage starts. Sometimes, if you have existing coverage on these conditions, they may not be counted. However this varies by state and insurer. Some states do not permit insurance companies from refusing coverage due to pre-existing conditions – and the rates are usually best for those with pre-existing conditions in states that have Community Rating, shown in Figure 2.6.

If you file a claim for a significant medical condition with the first few months or years of the policy that you did not know about or disclose, you may experience difficulty in satisfying your claims. Insurers are constantly on the lookout for those that buy health insurance knowing or suspecting a medical problem. They will go through prior medical records looking for any signs that you knew and didn't disclose the condition. However, this isn't a factor in employer groups, as they have guarantee issue polices that do not require medical underwriting of individuals when they become employees. Guarantee issue will also apply for spouses and children of the employee.

☼ **Best States to Buy Health Insurance if You Have a Medical Condition**
One of the biggest hurdles for people with a medical condition is being able to buy health insurance. Since employer policies generally cover anyone who is eligible regardless of health status, the employer group route is a good choice for people with a medical condition regardless of your state of residence. Some states also offer a period of time each year when individuals may be guaranteed issue of insurance from the state Blue Cross Blue Shield company (referred to as open enrollment), but again the rate is not guaranteed, so it may not be as affordable as other options.

State	Medical Underwriting?	Community Rating?	Guaranteed Issue?
Maine	No	Yes, but can vary based on age, occupation, geography, smoker status	Yes
Massachusetts	No	Yes, but can vary based on age, geography, benefit level	Yes, 3 products from each insurer
Michigan	Yes	No, except for Blue Cross Blue Shield of Michigan	No, except for Blue Cross Blue Shield of Michigan
New Jersey	No	Yes, but can vary based on age, gender, and geography	Yes
New York	No	Yes, but can vary based on family composition and geography	Yes
Oregon	Limited	Yes, but can vary by geography and benefit design	Yes, with 6 months creditable coverage
Vermont	No	Yes, but can vary by criteria approved by Insurance Commissioner	Yes
Washington	Limited	Yes, but can vary by age, geography, wellness, family size, and tenure in plan	Yes

Figure 2.6: Best States to Buy Health Insurance in if You Have a Medical Condition

Waiting Period

If you have a pre-existing condition, have not had health insurance just prior to coverage (usually within 63 days), or haven't had health insurance for a long period of time prior to coverage, insurers will make you wait before they'll pay certain expenses. Some insurers will have a waiting period for everyone. Sometimes this includes preventative healthcare in the first year of the policy, even when you've had

> ☼ **Five Ways to Get Guaranteed Issue Health Insurance**
> (Especially useful if you have a medical condition)
> 1. From your employer
> 2. From your spouse's employer
> 3. From your own small business policy
> 4. From individual insurers in your state that offer guaranteed issue
> 5. Move to a state that has guaranteed issue and community rating, buy insurance with a national network, and then visit your old home on a regular basis.

health insurance all your life. State laws govern some of these, and insurance companies can make choices about what they'll cover in concert with the state laws, or where state laws don't specify.

Eligible Expenses

Not everything that you might consider healthcare is going to be eligible for payment in your health plan. Additionally, the list of items eligible for tax treatment, such as for the federal itemized deductions or the HSA account, may not cover everything that you may want to spend money on. For example, chiropractic may not be covered in your health plan, but may be eligible under tax treatment, so if you had an HSA/HDHP, you could spend pre-tax dollars on your chiropractic care. Certain alternative treatments, such as some herbal treatments, may not be eligible at all.

> ☼ **On Being Rejected:**
> "That's the key problem to solve to make individual insurance work. Right now about 14% are denied coverage. Keep in mind that when families apply for coverage, a family of 3 or 4, it's typically one person that is being denied coverage for some reason. Typically it's some kind of chronic condition that one of the family members has: it could be a child or it could be an adult. One of the things that we tell these families is to get everybody else covered right away while you can, then let's try to figure out what we can do for that one person in the family that does have some type of pre-existing condition. In most cases, there are public programs available in many states that we can hopefully get that individual covered."
> "By excluding that 14-15% risk, you're keeping the prices affordable for the other 85% of people that need to buy health insurance. But we also have to take care of that 15% that have a pre-existing condition. Many states have high risk pools that are subsidized. In California, it's subsidized by tobacco, other states use health insurance premium taxes. These programs are not funded fully. High risk pools are a way to finance people in high risk. We should be using risk pools to target care to those people. The people in pools have diabetes, previous heart conditions, extreme asthma or allergy. These people need **well** managed care."
> - Bob Hurley, Senior Vice President of Carrier Relations, eHealthInsurance.com

Example Diagrams

Let's take a look at how the terms come together with some examples. These examples are based on plans that I found while shopping for health insurance. They are, of course, not necessarily the right combination for you. After underwriting, the rate might change depending on any significant health conditions. For illustration purposes, a typical doctors office network negotiated rate is listed at $55 – a rough rule of thumb I created for the shortest primary care doctor visit fees in my town. Specialists will be higher, and rates are probably higher many other places in the country.

Deciphering Health Insurance Terms:
Example 1

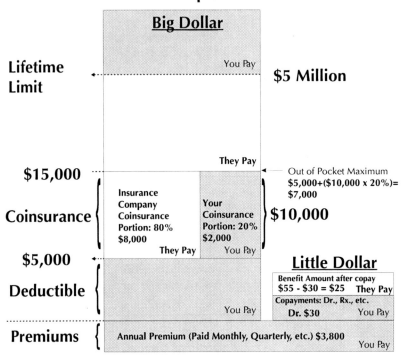

Figure 2.7: Diagram of Example 1

The first example in Figure 2.7 shows a plan with an annual premium of $3,800 (about $317 a month) that has a $5,000 deductible, 80% coinsurance on the next $10,000, a $5 million dollar lifetime limit, and no annual limit. The plan also has a $30 copay for doctors office visits, and no prescription coverage. From these numbers we can calculate that the total out of pocket for an individual is $7,000. For this plan the deductible and the coinsurance apply for two people – so for the whole family, if two people should have a problem in any given year, the total out of pocket would rise to $14,000. For a single incident that happened to span two calendar years, the total out of pocket would rise to $28,000. Or for an ongoing problem, for one family member, $7,000 a year. The dollars add up.

How would that look if we had a different plan – one that would reduce the amount of out-of-pocket year after year? Consider a plan at the other end of the spectrum.

Deciphering Health Insurance Terms:
Example 2

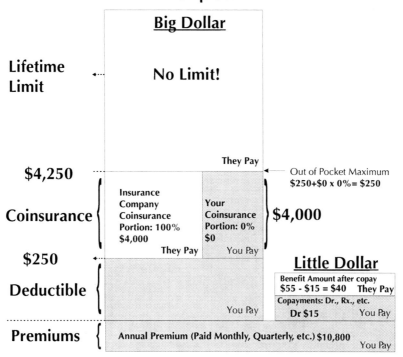

Figure 2.8: Diagram of Example 2

Example 2 in Figure 2.8 shows a plan with an annual premium of $10,800 (about $900 a month) that has a $250 deductible, 100% coinsurance (meaning that there is none – the insurance company pays everything after deductible), no lifetime limit, and no annual limit. The plan also has a $15 copay for doctors office visits ($30 for specialists), and three tier prescription coverage ($10, $35, $50) depending on generic, preferred, or name brand. From these numbers we can calculate that the total out of pocket for an individual is $250. For this plan the deductible applies for three people – so for the whole family, if three people should have a problem in any given year, the total out of pocket would rise to $750. For a single incident that happened to span two calendar years, the total out of pocket would rise to $1,500. Or for an ongoing problem, for one family member, $250 a year. The dollars don't add up nearly as fast in this plan, until you account for the difference in annual premium.

A third example shows yet a different plan. This one is a high deductible plan with an associated health savings account.

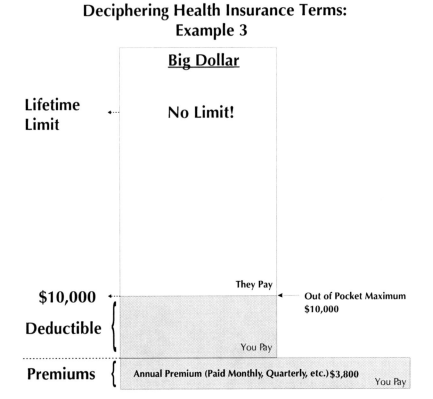

Figure 2.9: Diagram of Example 3

Figure 2.9 shows a plan with an annual premium of $3,800 (about $317 a month) that has a $10,000 family deductible, 100% coinsurance (meaning that there is none – the insurance company pays everything after deductible), no lifetime limit, and no annual limit. The plan has no copay or prescription coverage, although it does cover wellness care in full (meaning no copays). The total out of pocket for the family as a whole is $10,000. For a single incident that happened to span two calendar years, the total out of pocket would rise to $20,000. Or for an ongoing problem, for one or more family members, $10,000 a year. This plan is definitely geared for those with the ability to handle a large deductible – and it also has the tax advantages of an HSA – primarily the ability to put away $5,750 tax-free dollars a year into an IRA-like investment account, but you'd have to be making at least $50,000 per adult for the tax benefits to be of great value.

Medicare Examples

You've seen how a few example comprehensive medical plans compare for those not eligible for the most popular health insurance plan: Medicare. As you'll see from these diagrams, Medicare is closely modeled on the indemnity insurance plan – where you are responsible for a portion of the coverage, and have no upper limits on your financial responsibility. You may wish to create your own Medigap plan diagrams to see how they fill in the holes of the Medicare coverage – and determine if staying "in-network" is a fair trade-off for the reduced financial exposure provided by Medigap insurers.

Figures 2.10, 2.11, and 2.12 provide a diagram of the coverage provided by Medicare Part A, Part B, and Part D, respectively. No options are available for traditional Medicare Part A or Part B, unless you choose a Medigap policy that complements the coverage of Part A and Part B, or choose a Medicare Advantage managed care plan. Various options are available for Part D at different levels of coverage; the diagram presents one option that I found.

Deciphering Health Insurance Terms:
Example 4 - Medicare Part A: Hospital

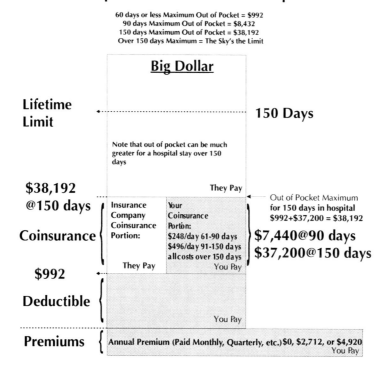

Figure 2.10: Diagram of Medicare Part A: Hospital

Figure 2.10 shows a diagram for coverage of Medicare Part A, the hospitalization coverage. The premium depends on a number of factors, but if you've worked 10 years, then you are likely to be eligible for Part A without paying any premium. There is a single deductible amount of $992 for the first 60 days of hospitalization, and a per-day amount for days 61-90, and a different amount for days 91-150. Coverage runs out after 150 days, and you'll need to pay everything after that. The amount you pay depends on the number of days in the hospital, and of course whether everything is a covered service. For a hospitalization of 60 days or less, your total responsibility is $992, for a visit of 90 days, you'd owe $8,432, and for 150 days in the hospital, your share is $38,192. Anything over this amount of days and you pay the full bill – or apply for Medicaid if you have little or no assets, which you may not after paying for hospital days starting at 151!

Deciphering Health Insurance Terms:
Example 5 - Medicare Part B: Medical

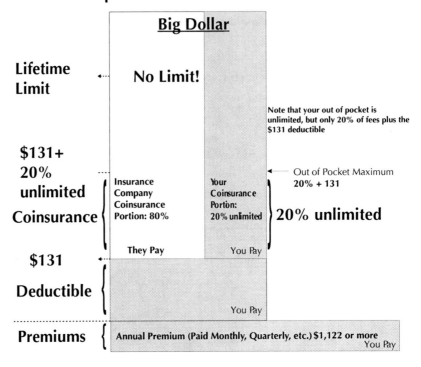

Figure 2.11: Diagram of Medicare Part B: Medical

Figure 2.11 shows a diagram for Medicare Part B: Medical. The premium is fixed to a month amount of $93.50 a month, with a higher rate for individuals whose income exceeds $80,000 and married couples whose joint income exceeds $160,000. There are few items that are offered with a copay – most services come in the big dollar column, where you pay 20% of the bills, after paying for the entire $131 dollar deductible. There is no upper limit on the amount of your 20% coinsurance.

Deciphering Health Insurance Terms:
Example 6 - Medicare Part D: Prescriptions

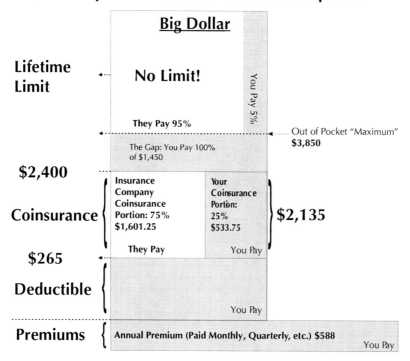

Figure 2.12: Diagram of a Representative Medicare Part D Prescription Plan.

Figure 2.12 shows a representative Medicare Part D prescription plan that costs $49 a month, or $588 for a year. You pay the first $265 in prescriptions at the discounted plan rate from a participating pharmacy, then 25% of the next $2,135 in prescriptions. After that you are responsible for 100% of the next $1,450, which is known as the "gap." After that, you only pay 5% of the balance of all the prescriptions that you consume in a calendar year.

Summary

Hopefully at this point you know how the dollars stack up with all the numbers being thrown at you during the health insurance shopping process. You may be starting to strategize about how you'll keep your money in balance with how much you'll pay in monthly premiums and in the case of a medical event. Visit www.BestHealthInsuranceBook.com to try some of the online tools for creating diagrams and determining good deals. In the next chapter we'll explore options on where to get your insurance.

Chapter 3

Where to Get Health Insurance

The first place that many people think of getting health insurance is at work. This is because health insurance originally started as a workplace benefit to attract and retain employees. However, with the trends in recent years, the workplace may no longer be the first or best place that you should look for health benefits. For those in excellent health, a private insurance policy bought outside the workplace may be a better choice for a potentially lower premium and the guarantee of maintaining that insurance when switching employers or losing employment. If in doubt, compare the monthly premium of an individual plan with what is currently deducted from your paycheck for your company plan. You may be surprised.

This chapter deals with the places that you can get insurance – and discusses working with an agent when you're exploring buying health insurance by yourself. Figure 3.1 gives a quick overview of some of the places that you can get health insurance for you, for your spouse, or for your dependents. Sometimes getting insurance from a combination of these sources provides the best deal.

Overview: Where to Get Health Insurance and Related Products

1. From Your Employer
   – While Employed
   – When You Leave Employment: COBRA and HIPAA
   – Early Retirement
2. From Your Spouse's or Partner's Employer
3. Private Health Insurance (Open Market)
4. Doing Without
5. Discount Programs
6. Health Benefit Plans
7. Government Programs

Figure 3.1: Summary of Where to Get Health Insurance

Read through the following sections to see which apply to your situation. Remember, you can mix and match and get health insurance for family members from different places. Keep in mind that it is easiest to get health insurance from some of these sources when you are healthiest. Health insurance is better to get when you are healthy – you get lower rates and more choices. However, if you have a medical condition, getting health insurance from an employer is easier and perhaps less expensive – if you can even make it to work when sick, or you can have a spouse go to work. When healthy, if you qualify for the best rates from a reputable insurer, you'll stay in the "best rate" category for the entire time that you keep the insurance policy from that insurer – even if you get sick. Lastly, be sure to check out the discussion of agents at the end of this chapter – since you will buy insurance from an agent, whether independent or working for a single insurer.

From Your Employer – While Employed

The best part of getting health insurance at work is that it seems to be a no-brainer. The health insurance policy is managed for you, with a limited amount of time and effort on your part. The employer deducts your contribution from your paycheck (before taxes), and generally takes care of all the details. But your choices are limited to what the employer selects and you may pay more for a "full-feature" plan than a "budget" plan would cost you if you bought it as an individual. Or you may be limited to a budget plan when what you really want is a full featured plan.

When the employer pays their part, typically about half of the fees, it might cost less than buying your own policy outside of work. However, if you ever leave the company and want to take the COBRA continuation (covered later in this chapter), you'll have to pay the full amount that the employer pays, plus two to three percent as an administrative fee. If you do this after you or a family member has become ill and has a medical condition, the rates that you'll pay once COBRA ends and you take a HIPAA guaranteed policy can be very high. Plus, if you don't play the COBRA and HIPAA continuation just right, then you may end up with no insurance or with extremely expensive insurance from a state high risk pool.

> ☿ The best time to buy health insurance is when you don't need it. Unfortunately, if you buy it from your employer, and leave employment due to medical problems, you won't have a chance to buy your own insurance when you're healthy, so it'll cost a lot more through COBRA, HIPAA, or individual insurance.

From Your Employer – When You Leave Employment

Sometimes when you leave your current employment you are already employed somewhere else. If they provide a health insurance benefit, you can simply transition to the new plan. However, if the new employer is too small to offer health insurance or you are going out on your own, you may be faced with the issue of what to do about health insurance. You may be able to continue on your current health plan for a period of time.

COBRA Continuation Coverage When Leaving Employment

The Consolidated Omnibus Budget Reconciliation Act, a U.S. federal law, provides for health coverage that continues for typically 18 months after a qualifying "event" such as leaving your job, though you get more time for certain special cases, such as disability. This only applies to employers above a certain size ,currently 20 employees, though some states have additional restrictions that apply to smaller employers. With COBRA, You'll end up paying no more than 102% or 103% (depending on your state) of the cost that the employer pays for the coverage, which will be more than you were paying as part of an employee share. My employer paid all expenses for healthcare when I was working there, so I had a significant jump in what I paid for health, dental, and vision

> ☿ **Timeline of Health Benefits When Leaving Employment:**
> - If no medical condition, get private insurance effective within 60 days.
> - If medical condition, determine how significant the condition from an agent. Then either buy private insurance, or take COBRA option (you've got 60 days). If you take COBRA option keep for maximum time (18 months for termination, 29 months for disability, 36 months for death or divorce), then buy HIPAA guaranteed for person with medical condition, private insurance for others.

when I left to start my own business.

It pays to be on the right plan before leaving employment if your employer offers more than one option. You pay the cost of the policy that you're on for the months that you keep it. You can, however, change during the election period that occurs once a year. My family was on the more expensive plan when I left my place of employment, and we changed plans during the election period. This was after I'd been on the more expensive COBRA option for 6 months. Unfortunately, we had already paid the higher rate for a plan that was more than we needed. If I had only done the paperwork at the right time we would have saved about a hundred dollars a month x 6 months = $600. The only reason I didn't was because all the paperwork seemed too confusing and time consuming at that time. In hindsight, a dumb reason.

You have a fixed period of time to apply for COBRA continuation coverage after leaving employment – currently 60 days. There are specific forms that you should get from your employer. You are then required to make payments yourself for the health insurance, sometimes to your employer, sometimes to a company that they use to manage COBRA enrollees. You are also responsible to ensure that the COBRA fees are paid at the beginning of each month. If you prefer, you can certainly pay for more than one month at a time, although keep in mind not all companies can handle multiple payments, so check with them before you send in the payment. Ultimately you are responsible for making sure that payments are received and credited for the right month. This may seem very straight forward to you, but most companies are not in the business of making sure that your COBRA payments are paid accurately. I know that I had to keep on top of this when I was on COBRA – checking that the payments were credited correctly each month. If you are more than 30 days late, you will probably lose your coverage.

Some state laws are more restrictive and have other issues around the coverage when you leave employment. However, they are only minor adjustments to the federal law – so don't expect to be given free insurance or get a longer term for COBRA. For example, Georgia has a rule that gives a 3 month COBRA type continuation when your employer is not required to offer COBRA using the federal guidelines. Check with your state to see what additional provisions they have when leaving employment.

> For more details about COBRA, frequently asked questions and their answers are provided by the U.S. Government Department of Labor at www.dol.gov/ebsa/faqs/faq_consumer_cobra.html More laws may also apply at the state level, so check with your state's department of insurance and department of labor.

HIPAA Coverage After COBRA Ends

At the end of COBRA continuation coverage, you can buy guaranteed coverage. The Health Insurance Portability and Accountability Act of 1996 known as HIPAA, provides the option to buy a HIPAA Individual Health Insurance Policy once the COBRA period runs out. HIPAA is guaranteed issue, but it may be significantly more expensive than other choices, if you're healthy enough to have other choices.

Guaranteed issue simply means you are guaranteed coverage, but not guaranteed a reasonable rate. Guaranteed issue insurance may be more expensive, so you may find a lower rate without guaranteed issue. If you are sick, have pre-existing conditions or less than healthy, then the costs may be higher no matter what type of plan you have. If so, guaranteed issue health insurance may be the best option.

If you end your HIPAA plan or the plan stops doing business in your state, then you are not guaranteed coverage on any new plan. My local health insurance agent told me that the HIPAA plans are more expensive and are not necessary for someone in good health, since many plans guarantee that they will renew your coverage just as HIPAA does. If you can secure non-HIPAA insurance, you may find it less expensive than a HIPAA plan. If you are healthy and you've got the time and energy, you can explore both options. If your health is borderline or poor, you must check both options and see which has the better rate and terms.

Why is guaranteed issue more expensive? Because it is an individual plan where the insurance company doesn't have a chance to adjust the rate based on health – so they use a number that represents the average cost of everyone in

> "$1,500 a month for a guaranteed issue HIPAA policy with a maximum $500,000 benefit – on the open market it is an unlimited benefit and costs less."
> -Jennifer McLaurin, Director of Sales, John F. Sipp & Associates

the HIPAA issued plan. They know that most people taking this plan have health issues because their existing pool of people in the plan tend to be sicker than those applying for insurance individually.

If you plan ahead (12 months or more) and create a new business for your departure (it should be profitable and not just a vehicle for health insurance), then you can try for a guaranteed issue small business group plan – which is available to small businesses with one or two employees (minimum) depending on the laws in your state. Of course, there are more requirements to having a small business group plan, most importantly making enough money to pay for the plan as well as for the expenses of your business.

Early Retirement Health Insurance When Leaving Your Employer

Fewer and fewer companies are offering health insurance to retirees, early or other. In some cases, a golden parachute or other special program may provide access to health insurance. These are usually set up during the hiring process, as part of a promotion, or in the event of a company downsizing. Sometimes if your employer really likes you, or the opposite when they really want you to leave without a scene, the employer can find some way to provide health insurance. This can also be the case during a significant layoff. However, be aware that the level of benefits and the amount that you are responsible for paying can change over time, unless you get an iron-clad in-writing contract saying it won't, and the changes are usually to your disadvantage, such as rising rates, copays, and declining levels of benefits. If you are paying for this coverage, it may still make sense to consider other options, as your share of the costs may increase to the point that another option may be less expensive.

Health Insurance from Your Spouse/Partner

If your spouse or life partner plans to continue working, you may be eligible for health insurance through his or her employer. You may already be covered under a spouse, family, or partner relationship in the plan, in which case, until you are eligible for Medicare or your spouse/partner leaves employment, you may have your health insurance source.

Similar to getting health insurance from your employer, the expense of this option may be high if the company has had a number of people with expensive medical procedures or if the plan is very extensive, with lots of bells and whistles. If the expense of this plan is high, then you might explore other options as presented below that may save you money and eliminate some of the more expensive choices. Keep in mind that the disadvantages to being on an employer plan apply to your spouse's plan, too. If you are healthy, buying your own individual policy may work out better in the long term.

Individual Health Insurance Policy

The first thing that you should do is to get the list of insurers from your state government insurance office or their website. I was able to find a list titled "Licensed Insurers Marketing Individual Health Insurance Coverage in North Carolina" and a separate list of companies that provide group coverage using the state resources listed in Appendix B. I found 16 companies selling these individual plans, half of which are selling policies only available if you join an association. I also found information about the number of people insured by each company. This was broken down by county, so I could see how many people in my area are on each plan. This is a good indicator of available doctors for the plan. The more people on the plan in your county, usually means more doctors to pick from. You can find statistics about complaints, including a ratio of number of complaints to the amount of business the insurance company is doing in the state. Needless to say but still worth repeating, avoid the companies with outrageously high complaint ratios. This is essential background information to be gathered before shopping for a policy. Use this list to eliminate the higher complaint companies, since the last thing you want is a hassle when you're sick. These steps and more are discussed in further detail later in Chapter 7.

> **Short Term Insurance**
> Short term plans can be useful. They can be effective immediately and can provide coverage between jobs. However, if you use one and get really sick, and you cannot get onto a guaranteed issue policy (for example from another employer or a spouse's employer), then your rate may be much higher or you may be denied coverage.

There are a lot of ways to buy health insurance on the open market. Once you have a list of all legitimate health insurance companies that sell individual insurance in your state, you can do any combination of the following to gather more information about policies from those insurers:

- Ask friends and associates, or look in the phone book for a health insurance agency.

- Go directly to a health insurer.

- Search on the internet for the health insurer or health insurance agencies.

- Check in with any associations to which you belong or might wish to belong.

Insurance Agent

If you want personal contact and someone who will guide you through the process and help select the best policy for you, find an independent agent or firm that represents more than one insurer. This can be especially important when one or more household members have a health condition. The agent can provide a comparison of policies available through different insurers and help get the process moving along. Keep in mind that not every company is represented by every agent, even at the same firm. Working with an agent is covered in depth later in this chapter.

Directly from the Insurer

Some of the insurers have websites that provide detailed information and quotes. Others simply provide a toll free number as a way to contact the insurer's agents. Even if you are using an independent agent, you may wish to contact the individual companies directly through the internet or telephone in order to get a quote and to find out if your doctor is in the plan. There's no sense in buying health insurance if you can't find a doctor that you like, or that the choices are so limited that you are not happy with the plan and do not get good medical advice.

I like to go to the insurers website to learn more. I can then go at my own pace without someone on the phone rushing me. I also found that through telephone contact I was not given all the possible options or information that I could find on the website – and was offered only the pricier products. If you cannot use the website, then request all the information be sent to you in the mail, email, or by fax. You can even request a copy of the policy ahead of time, though there may be some resistance from the agent or insurer to providing it since people seriously considering a policy are likely to go through the application process and then review the policy when it arrives.

I feel most comfortable working with a local independent agent who can talk about the various merits of the different insurers and make sure that my application is in good shape before submitting it. However, not everyone can find a local health insurance agent, and some people would rather do the search from home or their office or cannot make it to an agent's office. If this sounds like you, conducting the search over the telephone or internet are better options for you.

Internet

After searching the Internet, I found that there are four varieties of health insurance related web sites. These types, discussed further in Chapter 8, are:

- Websites that provide immediate online rate quotes, for a single insurer
- Health insurance shopping malls that provide immediate online quotes for many insurers,
- Lead gathering websites that take your information and put you in contact with an agent,
- Non-insurer sites that provide varying degrees of information, from full quotes to contact information only. Those providing quotes are actually agents for the quoted companies.

There are also many other health insurance related websites selling discount programs, association-based insurance, and plenty of scams. Any reputable insurer will probably be listed on your state's list of licensed insurers, or for some associations, by the state in which the association is located. After investigating many websites and associations, I found that many of the offerings end up being the same as the policies offered by the major insurers – information that you can get directly from the insurer or an agent.

It is also worth noting that Internet insurance sales are regulated no differently than any other type of health insurance sales. Insurers, agents, and agencies must be registered in your state in order to legally sell health insurance. Even if you are buying health insurance as part of an out-of-state association, the agent must still be registered to sell the insurance in your state and to issue the certificate of coverage in your state,

Doing Without Health Insurance

Going without insurance means that you may pay "full retail" at the doctor's office, as opposed to the discounted fees negotiated by the insurance companies. However, there are some exceptions, such as my local university hospital, UNC Healthcare, which has agreed to give a 10% discount to uninsured patients. Doctor's rates can also be negotiated as long as you do it before your appointment, but I can't tell you how successful you'll be negotiating with your doctor.

The greatest risk of going without insurance is if something major happens, leaving you on the hook to pay for it all. In this situation you might be looking at financial assistance to pay for it – probably a combination of a payment plan and certain fee reductions – if you are eligible under income/asset guidelines. You may also go into such a significant debt that you will be forced into a personal bankruptcy. A serious medical event is a leading cause of personal bankruptcy in the United States. In addition if it is an ongoing medical event, you may find it very hard to get affordable heath insurance at all. This leaves you with ongoing, accumulating medical bills.

> Bankruptcy is frequently related to medical bills and poor financial management. Estimates are that anywhere from 20% to 50% of personal bankruptcies are related to medical bills. Of those bankruptcies, roughly 20% didn't have health insurance, and 80% were underinsured.

Discount Programs

Health discount programs claim to provide discounts on many different types of services, leading you to believe that you may be getting tremendous discounts just like a health insurer would get. There are many health discount programs in the marketplace right now. Some of them are meant to supplement health insurance, some are meant to replace health insurance, and some of them represent themselves as health insurance to unwary consumers.

> "A discount plan: it's not health insurance and we have to explain that to people all the time. They can't afford true health insurance, so they'll buy the discount plan. We can't tell them not to buy it, but just to be careful."
> -Jennifer McLaurin, Director of Sales, John F. Sipp & Associates

I've seen a classified advertisement in our local newspaper under the "insurance" heading – "Tired of the high cost of health insurance ?" and offering plans at $59.95/month or $99.95/month. I've also seen flyers at other locations – the kind that has the telephone number on a tear tab at the bottom. The scariest thing is that many of the strips were torn off. These plans are not insurance, and offer discounts with a few providers who have a hard time attracting business any other way. Many do not provide any discount to the doctors that you may already use, and the costs are relatively high compared to the amount of benefit received. In my state, I can get an individual health insurance policy for myself for less than a hundred dollars a month – and that includes discounts all around, plus major medical and wellness care – why would I want to spend $60 to $100 for only discounts? The only reason I can think of is that people are afraid of the cost of health insurance and automatically assume that they cannot get a good legitimate deal.

Generally you may not need one of these discount cards. Some discount cards are included as extras to health insurance policies, simply offering discounts on services that are not covered by the insurance policy such as massage, dental, and cosmetic procedures. I have not seen a lot of providers participating with any of these cards.

Health Benefit Plan (Not Insurance!)

Insurance is regulated and requires time and effort to comply with regulations and deal fairly with consumers. Health benefit plans are a way around the red tape of insurance, and may offer a lower rate, but they also may be illegal and do not provide the necessary protections to the consumers needs.

The U.S. General Accounting Office published a report in 2004 describing these scams and how many were detected in the years leading up to the reports. It concluded that the number of sham "insurers" is on the rise. Just in case you think that this might be a way to save money on insurance, consider this: many of the shams don't end up paying claims, and those people with large medical bills while "covered" by the plans ended up not only owing money to the facilities that the plan was supposed to pay, but also are unable to get affordable insurance now because of their medical condition. Plus they have lost the money that they paid into the plans.

The plans are appealing, offering to save a noticeable though not tremendous amount of money on premiums. However, the dangers are great, and there are some simple ways to protect yourself, that are discussed here briefly and in Chapter 10.

- First and most important, only select a plan with an insurer licensed in your state – and make sure that you get confirmation that the insurer is licensed for health insurance from your state agency responsible for insurance. You may wish to refer to the list of insurers in Chapter 7 on Page 87 – some of which have many names – to help determine if a subsidiary is a valid part of a company. You can check online for updates to this list, or use a public records database to check on the ownership of companies.

- Second, even if a licensed agent offers a plan and explains that it is not insurance – don't buy it – and contact your state department of insurance to report the incident.

- Third – don't say it couldn't happen to you – it happened to me, and it happens to hundreds of thousands of people each year.

Government Health Insurance Programs

Government-run health insurance programs provide benefits or access to benefits for elderly, low-income, disabled, and otherwise uninsurable people.

- Medicare provides basic health insurance to eligible people 65 and over, with additional coverages available at additional cost.

- Medicaid is a state-run program that provides medical assistance to those with low income and low assets.

- The State Children's Health Insurance Program provides health coverage to uninsured children whose families would not otherwise be able to afford coverage.

- Some states also provide a high-risk pool for those who would not otherwise be able to get private health insurance. The programs tend to be very expensive, so eligible individuals may still not be able to afford health insurance through these programs.

Each of these programs is discussed briefly below, so that you may determine whether you are eligible for any of these programs.

Medicare

Medicare is the largest health insurance program in the United States, covering about forty million people who are 65 or older, under 65 and disabled, or have End-Stage Renal (kidney) disease. It has been expanded over the years to include the following parts:

- Part A – Hospital Health Insurance.
- Part B – Doctor and Outpatient Health Insurance.
- Medigap – Private Insurer product covers additional expenses not covered in Part A & B.
- Part C – Private Insurer HMO or PPO plans that include Part A, B, and sometimes Part D, though the insured may be confined to a network. Also known as Medicare Advantage.
- Part D – Private Insurer plan for Prescription Coverage.

Many people qualify for Part A due to their employment contributions. Part B is at extra cost, currently less than $100 a month and deducted from Social Security, Railroad Retirement, or Civil Service benefits. You can also purchase a Medigap policy from an insurer or purchase a Part C plan instead of combination of Part A, Part B, and Medigap. Part D can be purchased from a private insurer, and may be included in a Part C purchase. The techniques for getting a good deal in this book can also be used for purchase of Medicare plans – to compare the Part A/B/D Medigap with a Part C plan, including the deductibles, coinsurance, and total out of pocket. Much of what you need to perform research can be done from the www.medicare.gov website. The Medicare Program provides a list of Medicare insurers in your state, along with appropriate deductibles/coinsurance for the Medicare Part A plan.

Medicaid

People with an extremely low income or no income and with little or no net worth are eligible for state-run Medicaid programs, with perhaps other qualifications. This is healthcare funding as a last resort, when other benefits have run out or have been terminated, and you don't have a penny to your name. This should not be part of a "good deal" strategy unless you clearly qualify.

SCHIP

The State Children's Health Insurance Program (SCHIP) is a jointly funded effort by the U.S. federal government and the states to provide health insurance to children who do not have health insurance and whose families have very low incomes. The plans are administered independently by the states, so specifics will vary. In some cases, fees and cost sharing are required of the families. While this program is open to those who qualify by income, there may be specific rules and monitoring of those who drop private insurance in favor of the state program. The program also has limited funding, so there may be a waiting list.

Community Medical

Some states also provide community medical programs. These can be used by people with or without insurance, and provide a sliding scale of fees for those that use the services. The lower your economic resources, the less you pay. If you absolutely cannot afford to purchase health insurance, then using resources like these, along with other free or low-cost clinics and medical schools, can stretch your dollar even further.

Insurer of Last Resort

If your state does not require any insurer to guarantee that they will provide insurance, then there may be a special program for those people that would not be able to medically qualify for health insurance. However, these programs are often very expensive, and many people that cannot get insurance also cannot afford these programs. Since the programs may cost many times the amount of a quoted insurance (in North Carolina it may be up to seven times the quoted rate), the insurance may not be affordable. If you have insurance and a significant medical condition, then you may try to keep your health insurance any way possible so that you do not risk financial ruin.

Use a Health Insurance Agent

If you are going to buy your own individual insurance policy, a small business group policy, or even make an individual purchase of an association group policy, your best bet for help with the process is to identify a reputable independent insurance agent. This agent will be licensed with the state in which you reside, sell products from more than one company (hopefully many), and be able to work with you to find the best company and plan, and then give you the information that you need for you to get the best deal.

No matter where you buy your insurance, you will be buying it from an agent. That agent may work for a local firm, or from a remote location. The agent may sell insurance from one company and it's subsidiaries or from a variety of companies. If you buy it directly from an insurance company, you'll be working with an agent who is employed by the insurer. If you buy it over the internet, you'll be buying it from an insurance agency that uses the internet as their primary sales vehicle. I feel it is best buying from an independent agent that carries a number of insurers in your state. It's even better if they're local if you would like to work with them in person. Many people feel comfortable enough to work over the telephone and internet.

> ·ϙ· "Your agent can be your HR person and can help you file a claim, advocate for you, answer questions, and help to understand things."
> -Jennifer McLaurin, Director of Sales, John F. Sipp & Associates

Most states license health and life insurance agents with the same set of tests. However, you should purchase your health insurance from an agent that specializes in health insurance since it can be complex. Lists of local agents can be found by using the resources in the back of this book. Agents who are serious about health insurance will be members of:

- National Association of Health Underwriters (NAHU) or
- Association of Health Insurance Advisors (AHIA) part of the National Association of Insurance and Financial Advisors (NAIFA).

Another mark of the serious agent is professional designations, such as:

- Health Insurance Associate (HIA)

- Registered Health Underwriter (RHU)

- Managed Healthcare Professional (MHP)

- Registered Employee Benefits Consultant (REBC).

Serious agents can also be found at firms that specialize in health insurance.

There are some good reasons to use an independent agent, and as always, a few things to watch out for just to keep your agent on the level. A brief list of the reasons to use an independent agent, and some things to be aware of when buying is presented here, followed by steps to check on any agent that you may consider.

> "The best way to find a good agent is word of mouth. Ask your friends. Ask your realtor, since they know the area. Ask at the local chamber of commerce."
> -Beth B. Parrott, Owner, Parrott Insurance and Benefits

Reasons to Use an Agent

- You can get information about which insurers provide specific benefits.

- You can avoid insurers that have problems with specific conditions.

- It will be easier to complete the application.

- You can have any terms and limitations explained until you understand them.

- The agent can act as an advocate for you with any problems once you're insured.

- There is usually no extra cost. A few may have a small fee due to declining commissions and increasing costs of business.

- An independent agent is better than a "captive" agent that only works for one insurer. Even independent agents may not represent all of possible insurers in your state so you'll need to decide if you need to get information from more than one agent.

Watch Out For:

- An agent might be tempted to provide a more profitable plan for the agent that is less advantageous to you; however you will arm yourself with knowledge to make sure that you can act in your own best interest.

- An agent may not offer all companies' products, so there may be a better deal out there not offered by the agent. However, you will have a list of insurers in your state and can contact more than one agent if necessary.

- Some agents may use high pressure tactics to close the sale. If you gather all your information first and don't fill out an application for insurance until you've made a decision, you'll be less likely to succumb to pressure.

- You may end up buying more insurance than you need. However you'll be able to see how much you spend and how much you have at risk with various plans and make your best choice using techniques presented in this book.

Check the Status of an Agent

It is helpful to check that a person who is claiming to sell you health insurance or some other policy is licensed to do so. This is also a good way to find out how long a person has been licensed, and which companies or company they represent. Keep in mind that someone who represents more than one company may be able to provide more options, but sometimes representing more than one company is simply representing divisions of the same company. You can also find out if any disciplinary action has been taken against the agent, which might be a consideration in whom you use as an agent. You'll even find that agents located out of state must be listed as authorized to sell you insurance in your state.

> **"Simple Tips for Buying Health Insurance**
> 1. You can shop for health insurance like anything else. You don't have to get it at work or through the government.
> 2. Don't be afraid of high deductibles. Most plans are very comprehensive when you hit the deductible. Be smart: balance the deductible with the amount of savings that you have. You need to be able to sleep at night. This is a great way to keep premiums down.
> 3. HSA's are cool. Learn about HSA's. If you are buying a high deductible plan, see if a health savings account is good for you so that you have money set aside.
> 4. If you have a health condition that you think is going to be problematic, call and talk to a licensed agent. Find someone who won't put you into one specific product, but look at what is available from the state and private insurance programs. Do your homework and if you're not comfortable, find someone who you are comfortable with. There are many state and federal programs out there that you may be qualified for, and you just don't know it."
> - Bob Hurley, Senior Vice President of Carrier Relations, eHealthInsurance.com

Contact your state agency responsible for insurance listed in Appendix B and give them the agent's first and last name, plus town of residence or location of business. Or use the web sites listed in Appendix B and look up the information yourself. For example, the North Carolina Department of Insurance website for agent information is found at: http://infoportal.ncdoi.net/agent_search.jsp?TYPE=P and provides:

- Current licenses for the agent, including effective date

- Companies the agent is licensed to represent, known as "appointments" or "sponsors" along with the appointed date

- Any disciplinary actions taken against the agent

I used the agent status information to check on an agent for a friend. The email I sent is shown here as an example of the kinds of things you can learn.

An Email to a Friend

Dear Z,

The agent you named, Mr. John Doe, listed in Wilmington, NC, was licensed to sell life & health insurance, plus medicare supplement and long term care insurance in May, 2002. He handles a number of different health insurers in North Carolina, which is good – he'll shop around if needed. He does not handle Blue Cross Blue Shield of North Carolina, and I wonder why not, since it is the largest insurer in North Carolina. He also has had no regulatory action, which is good.

X Insurance Company is licensed to sell "association group coverage" health insurance in North Carolina. If my information is accurate about what they're selling, then this means that you do not actually have a policy with them, but an association has the policy. An association that they may control. You, however, have a certificate of coverage. Why does it matter? Because the policy can be modified and cancelled without your input. You are probably also part of a group of insureds who bought this insurance in North Carolina in the same year, same quarter, or some other criteria used to group the applications.

Your rate, while it may not provide other benefits that you desire, is actually quite low. But it may not stay that way. Association coverage for groups works something like this: The first year, everyone gets a great deal in the group, and everyone is happy, as long as any claims are paid and the insurer is still in business. The second year, there will be a rate hike, which will probably be composed of part cost of medical expenses going up, plus another percent that is built into their rate filings with the state (I saw one filing that would add 10% automatically plus the usual 10-12% annual increase – for a 20-22% increase after the first year – and that doesn't take into account increases as we get older – the breakpoints are roughly at 35, 40, 45, 50, 55, 60 for noticeable jumps in rates). Because of this rate increase, healthy people will leave association group coverage for other coverage (or get it through an employer), leaving a sicker pool of people behind – who will drive the rate up year after year. If you get sick on this plan, you'll be stuck in the plan, paying higher rates with your sick association-group. It is hard to find coverage that is reasonably priced once a person gets sick (unless of course it's through an employer – which cannot discriminate based on health status).

I'd love to hear what it is that you desire from health insurance. You have many options, including putting your kids and yourself on different plans if that option makes sense. What is it that you wish were different about your plan?

-Jonathan

Figure 3.2: Email to a Friend Shows Information Found on Agent.

Summary

You've seen where to get insurance and how to work with an agent. You know that you can choose a different place to get health insurance for each family member. Now you need to consider the features that you desire from a health insurance policy, which is the topic of the next chapter.

Chapter 4

How to Compare Features of Health Plans

Comparing features of health plans is a lot like looking at features on an automobile. When my wife and I were buying our first car together, we read *Consumer Reports*, pored over car brochures, and visited dealers. We test drove, negotiated a deal, arranged financing, and drove off the lot with a car that we thought was perfect for us. But we missed something important. Cup holders.

If you don't carefully study the features important to you, you too may end up with a car that doesn't have cup holders. There are many features to compare, and without looking carefully at each feature that is important to you, you may end up hating that part of the plan. Or driving a car without cup holders.

Getting Started

The first thing you need to do is to understand the different types of features that may be offered separately or in combination under plans available to you. A list of typical offerings is provided in Figure 4.1 to help you understand what is generally available so that you can jump-start your search.

Types of Features Generally Available on Health Plans

- Basic Features: Hospitalization, Outpatient Procedures, State Mandated Features
- Nationwide Network
- Wellness/Preventative Services
- Laboratory Work
- Pregnancy/Maternity
- Prescriptions: Generic and/or Name Brand
- Dental
- Vision
- Mental Health and Substance Abuse
- Alternative Medicine/Chiropractic/Acupuncture
- Accident & Life Add-Ons
- International Coverage
- Home Health Care
- In Network and Out of Network Coverage
- Limited/Unlimited Lifetime or Annual Benefits

Figure 4.1: Checklist of Typical Health Insurance Features.

It is important to note that the techniques in this book apply to many types of health insurance. However, this chapter focusses on the comprehensive types of health insurance. Single peril policies, such as those that only cover cancer, can be evaluated in the same way as any other policy according to the techniques in this book. The same goes for Medigap and

Medicare Part D prescription plans. While I can see that a few people will have a specific need for a single peril policy, and that most people on Medicare should seriously consider a Medigap/Medicare Part D policy, this chapter will focus on the bread-and-butter of health insurance: the comprehensive plan.

Plans can offer any or all of the features in Figure 4.1. But plans are not necessarily all equal in their coverage. For example, there may be a limit in the number of visits for mental health or chiropractic, and this limit may vary among plans and insurers. The number of physicians and facilities in networks will depend on the specific network, and also on how many are in a specific geographic region, especially important if you will be traveling frequently or living in more than one location during the year. You may also have a maximum benefit in a year, for example a $2,000 cap on prescription benefits, or a minimum amount spent prior to benefits kicking in, such as the deductible or a separate prescription deductible. Be aware that different companies can define a "year" differently: some as a calendar year, others as a rolling 12-month period. Some also put waiting periods in effect for services unrelated to pre-existing conditions, such as coverage for wellness visits provided after 12 months on the policy.

Take the example list in Figure 4.1 and check off those items that are essential to you. You can mark items that are "nice to have's" with a different mark, but remember that you will be paying for every feature in a plan, and if you don't use the feature then your money will not be well spent.

Next, make a grid of the features that are important to you across the top, and a list of insurance plans down the side. See the example in Figure 4.2. You may not have a list of plans yet – so wait until you start getting quotes in Chapter 8. Put a check mark in each feature that a plan has that meets your needs, a plus in each feature that exceeds your needs, and a minus in each

> ☿ "We make a spreadsheet comparing the features of different plans and present that to our client."
> -Beth B. Parrott, Owner, Parrott Insurance and Benefits

feature that a plan has, but doesn't meet your need. Put an X in those cells that don't have that feature in the plan at all. Once you've filled out the grid with all of your information, and possibly a few question marks for those plans that you can't figure out whether the benefit exists, you can narrow down those plans and insurers that will meet you needs. Those are the plans for which you should get quotes. Sometimes the quotes come at the same time as your research into the features, so make sure you read Chapter 8 and prepare that grid for the quotes before beginning your research. You can download a template at www.BestHealthInsuranceBook.com.

	Hospitalization	Outpatient Procedures	Nationwide Network	Wellness
Plan A	✓	✓	✓	+
Plan B	✓	✓	✓	–
Plan C	✓	✓	X	X

Figure 4.2: An Example Grid of Features Versus Plans.

The Basic Features

Most plans have similar basic features. They typically cover hospitalization, outpatient pro-

the basics

cedures, doctor's office visits, and related laboratory work. The plans provide coverage for significant medical problems that can lead to large medical bills. They generally are subject to an annual deductible amount that you commit to when you apply for a plan. However, the level and structure of the coverage will vary across plans. Some have specific per-day or per-illness maximums, some don't. Some have limited annual benefits, and others don't. When comparing plans, keep these factors in mind. Personally, I feel uncomfortable with an annual limit that may not cover a disastrous medical event – the biggest reason that I have health insurance.

You can also expect to see any state or federally mandated features listed on the plan, such as mammograms. These include features that by law must be included in any state plan. This list will vary by state, with some locations having few mandated features, and others many. If you don't see any state mandated features for your state, or see features listed for another state, proceed very carefully to review the plan since this may be a sign of a problem.

Is Your Doctor in the Plan?

Do you have a doctor that you already like or see regularly? If so, make sure that the doctor is on the plan. You can do this by looking at directories provided by insurers, but sometimes these can be out of date. They won't reflect changes that are about to happen. Use the directories, but check with your doctor's office. You can even do this if you haven't already picked a doctor, but have received recommendations from friends.

When calling a doctor's office, be sure to talk to the right person. Depending on the size of the doctor's office, there could be more than one person working with insurance companies. Ask for the insurance manager so that you can talk to the right person about the insurances that they accept. The person who answers the phone is more likely to be an appointment setter, and may not provide as much detailed information that could benefit you in your search.

Do this even if you're thinking that indemnity is more to your liking. You may find that the doctor's office has experience with several insurers and will know which one is more likely to cover their charges. Remember that the indemnity plan will likely only cover reasonable and customary charges. Your doctor's office may know which ones are more likely to cover their fees, primarily based on feedback from other patients.

It is also important to make sure that the doctor is accepting new patients under the prospective insurance plans. This may not apply to you if you already have an existing relationship with a doctor's office, but you need to be sure before changing insurance plans. Better to find out up front that a doctor is not going to accept anyone else with a certain insurer then after you've already made the switch.

You may also find that your doctor works out of several locations with the plan. Ensure that you can see the doctor at your preferred location, and with the highest level of coverage. Some doctor's offices that are part of a clinic or hospital may not be covered in the same way as a doctor's office away from these facilities. In fact, your visits to a doctor within a clinic or other larger facility may not be covered at all until you have met your deductible, or they may have a facility or service charge each time you visit the clinic – a costly mistake if you have to learn it the hard way.

Doctors may be considered primary care under one plan and a specialist under another plan. This may mean that access is limited, as with an HMO, or access fees higher, as with a copayment under plans that offer copays.

Keep in mind that plans can change over time. This includes which doctors and treatments are part of a plan, along with how they classify facilities. For example, a boy I know with a cardiac condition that requires annual monitoring used to see a doctor in a clinic and get annual tests with one copayment. But due to a reclassifying of the facility, the boy's family must now meet the deductible before any benefits are paid for the same annual visits in the same facility.

Wellness/Preventative Services

If you want your car to last, then you've got to change the oil, coolant, and perform other maintenance. Same for your body. If you want to get the most years and get the most from those years, you can't skip the wellness visits.

Either you get wellness care as part of your plan or you pay for it out of your own pocket separately. You are more likely to get preventative care if it is included in your plan, and according to the Institute of Medicine, you are statistically more likely to live longer when you have medical insurance, have your wellness visits, and seek healthcare when ill. You should plan on either budgeting for this expense on your own or buy it through a health plan.

There are some variations on what is covered, so make sure that you get what is important to you and recommended by a doctor that you trust.

Laboratory Work

Laboratory work when in the hospital may be covered under your plan, after deductible of course, and laboratory work for wellness visits may be covered under your wellness benefits. However, other laboratory work when you are ill outside of a hospital, including radiology and doctor fees to read x-rays, may not be covered until you pay your deductible amount. Some fully loaded plans cover all lab work, and have exclusive arrangements with specific labs; others offer options to have a limited amount of lab work done before the deductible applies. Some plans may cover everything that happens during a doctor visit within the doctors offices with a single copayment; others may leave you to pay each charge separately. If the laboratory that you use is within the network, then the negotiated fees may be a fraction of the list price, and you'll have a huge savings just from using an in-network laboratory.

Pregnancy/Maternity

Pregnancy/Maternity benefits are optional in some states, and mandatory elsewhere. These benefits cover healthcare from pregnancy through birth, and can be an expensive option to a plan. This is not to be confused with any fertility treatment, which I have not found on many plans. Some plans have a flat fee for a natural birth, with a higher amount for a cesarean section birth. Further, some plans offer a one-time copay for a birth, which covers all visits, lab work, and the child birth, regardless of the type of delivery. Once the baby is born, it can usually be added to the parent's plan within 30 days without any medical underwriting.

Prescriptions – Generic and/or Name Brand

Prescription coverage is necessary only when the expected expenses of prescriptions (name brand or generic) would exceed the amount paid for any copays and premiums paid during the year. Prescription benefits are also subject to many limits, so you must carefully weigh these options.

If you are healthy without any major ongoing prescriptions, you may do better without this coverage. You can still save money with bundled discounts that come with many plans, and also use generics. For example, one doctor I know asks patients what type of prescription coverage they have when diagnosing respiratory infections. If the patient has significant prescription coverage, he prescribes the 3-day name-brand antibiotic treatment; otherwise he prescribes the usual 10-day generic prescription. Even with excellent prescription benefits, the name brand treatment may mean a $25 prescription copayment, versus a generic cost of about $6 for the other treatment.

If you have an ongoing medication need, and are considering prescription coverage, keep in mind that having the condition in the first place may mean that you pay higher insurance premiums, or may even be rejected. The insurers know the costs of the medication and factor that into their underwriting. That's why you shouldn't go through this process alone, but consider working closely with a licensed health insurance agent who represents several insurers to ensure that you don't get rejected and to help you get your best deal.

Dental

Dental Insurance Good Deal Calculator

To figure out if dental is a good deal for you, go to www.BestHealthInsuranceBook.com, and find the "Dental Insurance Good Deal Calculator." You'll want to fill out the form for the fields that you obtain from any dental quotes. Call your dentist and get the cost per cleaning, cost per x-ray, and an estimate of how much the insurer usually pays for these services. You may need to convert the amount paid by the insurer to a percent by dividing the amount paid by the amount charged by the dentist. Then take the information from the dental quote: the monthly premium, the individual deductible, and number of family members subject to the deductible before the insurer pays in full, and the percent that they'll cover for other services. You can then see how much you'd need to spend on dental services for one, two, or three family members before you get back everything that you've paid in dental insurance. You may also be interested in noting the annual maximums that the policy will pay, per person and for the whole family, before you make your decision.

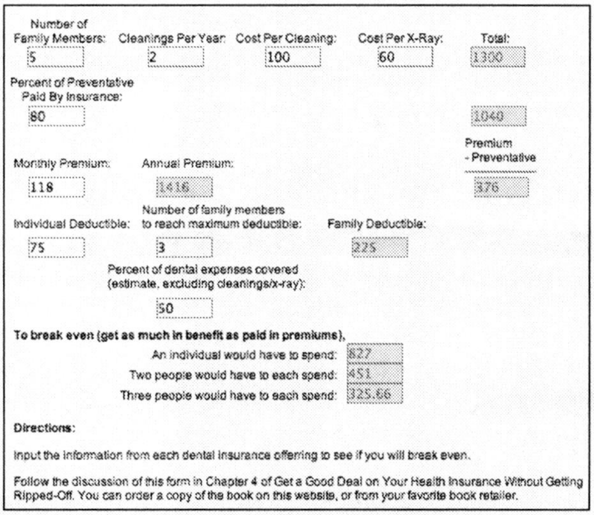
Number of Family Members: 5
Cleanings Per Year: 2
Cost Per Cleaning: 100
Cost Per X-Ray: 60
Total: 1300
Percent of Preventative Paid By Insurance: 80
1040
Monthly Premium: 118
Annual Premium: 1416
Premium - Preventative: 376
Individual Deductible: 75
Number of family members to reach maximum deductible: 3
Family Deductible: 225
Percent of dental expenses covered (estimate, excluding cleanings/x-ray): 50
To break even (get as much in benefit as paid in premiums),
An individual would have to spend: 827
Two people would have to each spend: 451
Three people would have to each spend: 325.66
Directions:
Input the information from each dental insurance offering to see if you will break even.
Follow the discussion of this form in Chapter 4 of Get a Good Deal on Your Health Insurance Without Getting Ripped-Off. You can order a copy of the book on this website, or from your favorite book retailer.

Figure 4.3: Dental Insurance Good Deal Calculator

Dental is an option that can be added onto a health plan or purchased separately. The insurance may cover preventative, up to a certain dollar amount, and then pay a much smaller percentage of any dental work needed, again with limitations and exclusions, such as what happened when my daughter needed a sealant replaced on a tooth and it wasn't covered.

Only the initial sealant was.

You may find that dental insurance works to your advantage if you anticipate seeing the dentist frequently for things other than cleanings. Otherwise, the cost of the insurance comes out to roughly the cost of visiting the dentist for cleanings twice a year, plus the x-rays, and then add about 10-20% extra. The upside is that if you have fillings, crowns, and so on, you may get reimbursed for up to half the expense when you have these procedures, but you must go through the effort to file claims, and anticipate that they won't all be paid.

Your alternatives to dental coverage are to save your own dental fund, either separately or together with the rest of your "rainy day" money, and/ or to make use of payment plans offered by the dentist or through a third party credit company. This is also another area where you can use HSA dollars to pay for items. Look at all of your options before assuming you need dental insurance.

> ϙ Don't have the cash to pay for dental work or a cosmetic procedure? Your provider may have payment plans available, or participate with a finance company that allows you to make payments.

Vision

Vision coverage is usually for prescription eye-wear, contact lenses, and so forth. Many plans include eye injury and disease (such as cataracts, glaucoma, and macular degeneration) as part of the hospitalization/outpatient coverage, so this vision coverage is really an extra for eye-wear and annual checkups. If you and your family members wear glasses, contacts, or have a family history of this type of treatment and need frequent changes in prescriptions, then it might work out financially to get this coverage. For savings, you could shop around for an optometrist/ophthalmologist and then get the eye-wear from a national discounter for less than the cost of this coverage. Some plans also offer a discount card for vision needs. If you select an HSA/HDHP plan, then you can purchase eye-wear and eye exams using money from your HSA with dollars that have not been taxed.

Mental Health and Substance Abuse

This is usually the weakest benefit of any plan, if it is even offered. There may be a dollar maximum, a limitation of inpatient/outpatient care, a limited number of visits per year, or a limitation on the conditions for treatment. Some networks may offer contracted rates for services, even if the service is not covered in the plan, which can amount to significant savings. You can use HSA funds to pay for these bills, but otherwise you are basically uninsured in this area, and must use whatever financial tools available to pay for healthcare, including payment plans and financing from bank loans.

Alternative Medicine/Chiropractic/Acupuncture

More plans are offering features in this area. However, they are not always available to individuals, but rather as part of a group plan. Even if they are offered, you may do better to manage the finances yourself, using your saved, possibly HSA, dollars and payment plans, since the bills come over time and do not generally reach into the stratosphere. Besides, many of these practitioners are accustomed to being "not covered" by insurance plans and offer payment plans, monthly flat rates, and other ways to make the treatments affordable. Your preferred practitioner may not even participate in any health insurance plans.

Accident & Life Add-Ons

Since you are shopping for insurance, why not look at accident and life add-ons? The biggest reason is that you can probably do better shopping for your life insurance separately from your health insurance. Life insurance and health insurance are different products. Heath insurance is meant to keep you alive and healthy, and life insurance only pays once you're past the need for health insurance.

Commissions for life insurance can be significantly higher than those for health insurance, so whomever is selling health insurance to you has a significant incentive to sell life insurance at the same time. Since states tend toward licensing insurance agents as both life and health, you may encounter this sales pitch. Stick to the task at hand and do your life insurance shopping separately.

International Coverage

If you travel outside the country frequently or for extended periods of time, then look for a plan that offers international coverage as a standard or optional benefit. If you don't travel abroad, and you have the choice, save your money and don't buy it. You can buy short term international travel insurance if the need arises, and not pay for it each month when you are home.

Home Healthcare

You may suffer a health event that could either keep you in the hospital for an extended stay, or allow you to continue treatment at home. Some hospitalizations may be short, but require continuing care at home. An example of this type of health event is a hip fracture that requires a full or partial hip replacement that may have a hospital stay of 3 to 5 days. This is followed by a few weeks in a rehabilitation center, and then perhaps months of at-home healthcare, with home visits from nurses, physical therapists, and occupational therapists. You may also need to purchase or rent durable medical equipment, such as wheelchairs and dressing aids. Your insurance coverage may be limited for those benefits received outside of a hospital or doctors office. Home healthcare coverage is intended to pay for your care at home in this type of situation. You may be able to forgo this coverage if you have enough money in a rainy day fund, lots of support from family and friends, and low risk factors for problems that might lead to an extended recovery.

In Network and Out of Network Coverage

For managed care plans (HMO, PPO), you'll find that the network may cover everyone that you'd expect to see in your area, and possibly throughout the country. Or you may find that the network only covers some types of healthcare and that providers may be limited in where they practice. For example, if you went on a ski trip to Colorado, your coverage may not apply to all services that you might receive in that area, yet that's when out of network coverage would be very valuable.

When considering this option, think about how frequently you may be out of network, and what types of activities you may be involved in outside of the network that may lead to injury or other health problems. Your coverage outside of a network will not be without hassles, however. You will probably be required to settle your bills with the provider at the time of the service, and then apply for reimbursement. If you have a credit card you can finance your costs for the month or two that a typical claim may require for processing. Certain charges may not be allowable anyway, so you'll need to pay for these out of your rainy day fund.

Limited/Unlimited Lifetime or Annual Benefits

Obviously unlimited benefits are preferable, but sometimes limits are offered in conjunction with a plan that has a very attractive rate. Lifetime limits apply to the lifetime of the policy, which may not coincide with your lifetime. You can obtain coverage elsewhere if you were ever to exhaust these limits, although you may need to be creative in where and how you obtain coverage if you are facing medical bills of this magnitude. However, if annual limits are not large enough, you may be in financial jeopardy for a medical event that exceeds that amount in a year. For example, many transplants run into the hundreds of thousands of dollars, so a policy that has a $100,000 annual limit and does not have any additional transplant coverage will not adequately cover a transplant.

Summary

You've seen ways to gather information about health plan features, and a way to score the plans based on which meets your needs. As always, more features tend to cost more money. The best way to determine what features you need is to look at what features you have used and then determine whether those features would include what you reasonably expect your medical needs to be in the future. While you are digging into the depths of your memory or medical records, you also need a picture of your health spending in the past in order to project that into the future – the subject of the next chapter.

Chapter 5

Anticipated Yearly Expenses

It is valuable to know what your health spending has been in the recent past since it helps you to predict how it will be in the future. Think of a family vacation, where you've stayed at hotels and bought gas, meals, and souvenirs along the way. You've got a spending pattern that is likely to continue along the way for the rest of your trip. Knowing about how much you've spent will help you to figure out how much more you'll spend until the end of the vacation. You need to have an idea of what your health spending might look like in the future if you want to get the best deal on health insurance.

A look within the last year is sufficient for most people, but information from the last few years can be even more helpful if things have happened over a longer time frame and may happen again. However, a year is really all that's necessary, so long as you have had your annual wellness visits within that year. If you look at less than a year, you'll miss out on those annual wellness visits and have to guess how much you would spend in a year.

You need to know how much money you have spent out of your own pocket. You need to know how much benefit you've received from any insurance coverage and discount programs. You need to see your total amount of spending on health items including copays, deductibles, coinsurance, non-covered items, and even the premiums. Knowing these things can be a big help when trying to predict your healthcare spending in years to come.

If you add up the amount that you spend on premiums, along with the other healthcare spending that comes along in the year, like copays, deductibles, coinsurance, and things that are not covered, and compare your plan to other plans, you can see that you might have saved a lot of money if you had chosen other health plan options. Armed with this knowledge, you are in a good position to compare various options and get the best deal on your health insurance.

Predicting what your health needs may be in the coming year can be very difficult, but there are a few tricks to make it easier. It is an educated guess, based on how you spent your healthcare dollars this past year and with the added benefit of knowing how things are going and whether there may be any problems.

> **Take the Express Route**
> If you want a quick estimate that is customized for your family, use the website www.healthpartners.com/empower/costofcare/ and choose the annual planner. You'll be asked questions and typical costs will be filled in for you. Also included is information about the typical costs for a medical conditions that a family member might have.

When estimating what your expenses will be for the next year and beyond, you can go about it a few ways. One way is to take a total of all the expenses from prior years and then make any adjustments based on your best guess. You can do this from a set of records, either on paper or the computer, or you can try to guess at what you spent.

Gather Your Most Recent Expenses

So how do you go about gathering all your healthcare expenses for the past year? It depends on what kind of record keeper you are. If you've got healthcare records for everything, then it's just a matter of filling in a worksheet. If you've got nothing, then you'll need to do some detective work to figure out what got spend where and when. If you're like me, you're somewhere in the middle, and can combine all of the approaches below to gather a reasonably good set of healthcare spending information – good enough to help you figure out what your best deal is going to be.

You don't need to make this a calendar year, just a 12 month period. Finding the information shouldn't be too painful, just use a combination of the methods to gather the best information that you can to support your worksheet. The first two methods presented work only if you have had insurance for a number of months, 12 months or more for best results.

Paper Explanation of Benefits (EOBs)

If you're a filer, and have everything on file, then pull out your Explanation of Benefits (EOB) records for the past year. An Explanation of Benefits is the paper that the insurer sends you after each doctor/facility visit that shows how much was charged, how much the insurer is paying, and how much you have to pay. You'll also need to retrieve your prescription receipts that show the prescription, the copayment, and the list price of the prescriptions.

I thought I was a filer, and looked in my files and in the to-be-filed box. I couldn't find EOBs for things that I knew had happened. So I used the next technique to gather the missing information.

Online Explanation of Benefits (EOBs)

If you're like me, you put the Explanation of Benefits (EOBs) that you got in the mail into the to-be-filed box, filed some, and probably lost others. If you still have a policy with the insurer and access to a website from the insurer, you may be able to download explanations of benefits from the website. If you don't have the same insurance, or the website doesn't provide EOBs, then you can call the insurer's customer service and request information. You'll want information about all of your benefits for the 12-month period, including who was treated, the doctor/facility, dates, billed amount, amount paid by the insurer, and how much you paid to the provider.

Provider Statements

You may have bills and/or statements in your files or elsewhere that you can use to figure out the same information that is included in the explanation of benefits documents. These are typically from a doctor or hospital and contain the information you need: who was treated, the doctor/facility, dates, billed amount, amount paid by patient, and amount expected due from insurer if a claim was filed with an insurance company. If an insurance claim was filed and the insurer has paid, you may receive another statement showing how much the insurer paid, and then an amount that the facility provided as a discount or write-off to zero out the balance. You may also find that some of the charges are not eligible, meaning insurance doesn't pay, and you must. In addition, if any out-of-network or indemnity amount exceeds the usual and customary amounts, you'll probably see that on the statements too, and you are likely to be responsible for paying that amount.

Checkbook/Credit Card Statements

If you don't have any other records, or were uninsured, look at your checkbook, credit card statements, or personal finance software to make a list of the expenses. This is more limiting because it only shows the dates and amounts that you paid, not any of the other useful information like who was treated, and how much of a discount was provided. You can use your checkbook and/or credit card statements to find out the providers and dates paid in order to go to the provider for more information.

Information from Providers

If you don't have any idea or have few records, don't despair. Most of the doctors/facilities keep their records around for a very long time. They are also reasonably open to providing statements of your account, which is a typical function of most businesses. You may request this either by visiting the office, over the telephone, or by mail. If you are gathering information for a spouse, the provider may require the spouse to provide a release of the information because of the privacy rules. You'll need to gather the same information: who was treated, dates, amount that they charged, amount paid by insurance, and amount paid by you. This should all appear on a typical statement from a provider.

Make Your Expense Table

Now that you've gathered the information, you need to put it into a form that you can work with. Using lined paper, make columns for each of the data gathered, or use a spreadsheet. Expense Table templates can also be found at www.BestHealthInsuranceBook.com.

Put the expenses into the list, including columns for the family member, the date of service, the provider's name, the full amount charged by the provider, the amount that the plan pays, and the amount that you pay. If you've got managed care, note that the amount that you pay and the amount that the plan pays are likely to be significantly less than the full charge billed by the provider.

Who	Type	Date	Doctor	Charge	Plan Pays	Patient Responsibility
Lisa	Sick	4/12/2006	Specialist	$244.00	$134.14	$10.00
Marge	Wellness	4/28/2006	OB/Gyn	414.00	174.37	10.00
Marge	Wellness	4/28/2006	Lab Work	72.00	22.64	0.00
Marge	Wellness	4/28/2006	Lab Work	114.00	6.95	0.00
Lisa	Wellness	5/22/2006	Pediatrician	249.71	156.52	10.00
Lisa	Sick	6/23/2006	Pediatrician	88.00	41.22	10.00
Marge	Sick	7/5/2006	Specialist	120.00	38.65	10.00
Maggie	Wellness	7/17/2006	Pediatrician	155.00	79.04	10.00
Maggie	Sick	7/23/2006	Specialist	244.00	141.06	10.00
Maggie	Prescription	7/23/2006	Pharmacy	125.95	113.35	30.00
Homer	Sick	9/17/2006	Specialist	623.00	482.38	10.00

Who	Type	Date	Doctor	Charge	Plan Pays	Patient Responsibility
Maggie	Wellness	9/21/2006	Pediatrician	146.00	73.92	10.00
Marge	Sick	10/14/2006	Specialist	404.00	270.00	10.00
Homer	Sick	11/19/2006	Specialist	70.00	42.17	10.00
Lisa	Sick	12/19/2006	Pediatrician	138.00	72.66	10.00
Bart	Wellness	12/23/2006	Pediatrician	215.00	98.47	10.00
Marge	Sick	1/3/2007	Family Practice	118.00	42.78	10.00
Maggie	Wellness	1/20/2007	Pediatrician	225.00	107.69	10.00
Homer	Wellness	2/14/2007	Family Practice	182.00	100.80	10.00
Bart	Sick	3/29/2007	Pediatrician	191.00	87.26	10.00
Homer	Sick	3/31/2007	Family Practice	98.00	55.85	10.00
			Total	$4,236.66	$2,341.92	$210.00

Figure 5.1: Example Table of Previous Year Health Expense

Figure 5.1 provides an example of the finished product that you can generate for investigation into your health expenses in a prior year. This is a fictional summary, although it is based on actual explanation of benefit statements. It serves to illustrate amounts spent by a fictional family of five.

There are 21 medical expenses listed in the example table. Of these, only one is a prescription. They are listed in date order, and have the total list price charge from the doctor/facility. These charges are submitted to the insurer, and if the doctor/facility is in a network, like the example above, the amount paid by the plan is listed, followed by the amount that the insurer determined should be paid by you. All of these examples items involve copays, however the last column could just as easily have larger dollar amounts that represent your portion of a deductible or coinsurance.

How to Make Use of the Table

From the example, you can see that the health plan paid $2,341.92 and the family paid an additional $210, totaling $2,551.92 against a healthcare value of $4,236.66 at list price. That's pretty good, nearly a 40% discount on all the healthcare received for being part of a network.

Now assume that healthcare premiums for this plan were $12,000 for the family for the year, a high amount, but reasonable for a big full featured corporate type of healthcare plan. If there was a plan that had a $20 copayment but only cost $10,000 a year, how would it look? The copayment section of the chart would double to $360, and the rest would stay the same. However, overall your expenses would be reduced, an increase of $180 on copays and a reduction of $2,000 in premium, an overall savings of $1,820.

Now look at how the numbers work if you were to have an HSA/HDHP policy with a $10,000 annual deductible and an estimated annual premium totaling $4,000. You'd have a reduction in premium of $8,000 from the full-featured plan, but an increase in the expenses that apply to the deductible. Instead of paying $210 in copayments, you'd pay the $2,551.92 in expenses, a difference of $2,341.92. The final difference in premium plus expenses is $8,000 − $2,341.92 = $5,658.08. A savings of $5,658.08! You could invest this amount in your HSA account (subject to annual maximums) and add to it year after year for any unforeseen health expenses. The only caveat to remember is that you are responsible for the full deductible amount each and every year that you have significant medical expenses.

There are also other totals that can be useful. For example, you can total by person which can help to determine whether a sicker or healthier person might be better insured separately from others in the family. You can total by sickness/wellness visits to determine how much a wellness benefit may be worth to you. You may also wish to total the doctor/facility separately from the prescriptions if you have a significant amount in either of these. This will aid in the process of determining the best plan, covered in Chapters 8 and 9. If you want to be extremely thorough, you could also include dental and vision to see if you should purchase coverage for each of those options. You can also try online tools at the book website found at www.BestHealthInsuranceBook.com.

Estimating Future Expenses

Now you can use the prior year information to guess how things might go in the next year. There are a few ways to go about this. First, determine whether this coming year you will be spending the same as amount as last year, more than last year, or less than last year. For example, if you have no known health issues and don't have any advance knowledge about anything that might cause a problem, such as a ski trip that might go bad or an upcoming sports competition, then you may say that it will be the same. If you had a ski trip with a broken leg and have given up skiing, then you may guess that you'll have fewer health expenses this year. In this case, you may take expenses related to the broken leg out of your total and use that as a starting estimate for next year.

> ☼ If you are planning on having a baby, or the possibility exists, make sure that you have maternity coverage before getting pregnant. You should also understand the policy coverage and options for a new baby, in case of any problems. Most babies are born healthy, but those that are born early or with a medical condition need lots of expensive medical care and can be added to the mother's plan within 30 days with not medical underwriting.

Known Issues

If you have any known health issues, then you may be able to get professional advice about what to expect in the coming years. If it is a significant issue, you'll know that you are probably going to need to explain carefully the condition to any potential insurer, and they'll certainly know how expensive the condition can be. The insurer will charge accordingly, raising the rates if appropriate, and they may not even underwrite the condition. Work with your agent to determine the best insurer, and whether exclusionary riders would help.

Unknown, but Possible

You can guess about things that might happen, however unlikely they may be to occur. These are things like a broken limb for kids, a back injury for an adult, or any other type of injury that people with your lifestyle may experience. You'll need to guess at how much that might set you back. Resources that give an idea of the cost of medical treatments for various conditions are provided in the appendices. These guesses are only to get an idea of what you might face financially so that you can insure yourself properly just in case.

Worst Cases

You'll also want to know the worst case scenario. This might be where an extremely rare issue comes up and requires very high expenses, in the million dollar and up range. This is where the insurance is really critical. Understanding what the expense might be, even though it is rare, and how it might be covered under various plans, is essential to making sure that you are prepared with the appropriate insurance. To take an extreme example, a million dollar medical bill where insurance only pays 80% would leave you responsible for $200,000, far more than most of us can afford. In Chapter 8, part of the financial comparison is to see how much a worst case would cost you each year, and then also year after year until you become eligible for Medicare.

> ☼ Did you know that you have a choice in terms of the treatment for injuries and illnesses that could make a huge difference in cost? For example a typical hip replacement will require several days in the hospital, followed by a few weeks in a rehabilitation center, and then months of physical therapy. An alternate procedure, has a day or two in the hospital, then home with a few weeks of physical therapy. The cost savings here are in reduced hospital time, no rehabilitation time, and less physical therapy

Summary

Now that you know what your medical spending looks like, it is time to consider whether you should go for individual or group insurance, the subject of the next chapter.

Chapter 6

Individual or Group Health Insurance?

Typically people have had group health insurance at work, and in the past getting on a group health plan would mean a lower cost and higher benefits. Before starting this book, I assumed that you still get a better deal on a group health insurance plan. However, the world has changed and some people, mostly those with few or no medical conditions when applying, are getting better deals on individual health insurance. In addition, the group insurance marketplace has really opened up for small businesses if you happen to own one or start one after reading this chapter.

There are four basic types of health insurance coverage that are available to most people who are not yet eligible for Medicare:

- Individual health insurance policy

- Individual purchase of association group coverage

- Individual coverage as part of an employer policy

- Group coverage in your own company group policy

> "As long as you pay your premiums you can keep your health insurance plan until 65. This includes children, until 18 or later if in college, then the child can convert."
> -Jennifer McLaurin, Director of Sales, John F. Sipp & Associates

A brief overview of each these four types of coverage is given, followed by a detailed table of the positive and negative aspects of the type of coverage. Each type of coverage has advantages and disadvantages. The trick is to find the right one for you.

The table in each section shows the pros (+) and cons (-) of a set of points for that type of coverage. Each table is structured the same so that you may see how each comparison point looks in each type of coverage. There is also a summary table at the end of the chapter to make comparison between the types of coverage easier.

For example, the first point deals with whether medical underwriting is part of the application process for each of the types of coverage. You can look at each type of coverage to see whether medical underwriting is involved. Medical underwriting is mostly a negative for you, because of the hassle involved, and if there is any medical history, it may mean a higher rate. However, it could be a positive if you are in perfect health when you get a lower rate, in spite of the hassle.

For those points where there might be a different answer for those with good health and those with health issues, the rating for those in good health is presented first, followed by a slash, and then the rating for those with health issues. In some cases there is not a + or – that applies because the point may not be clearly positive or negative.

Your task is to determine which of these types of coverage may work for you. Remember, you can combine the types of coverage, with different plans and types of coverage for each family member, in order to get the best deal.

Individual Health Insurance Policy

An individual health insurance policy is one that is issued to you. It provides coverage to you and any additional insureds, such as a spouse or children, on one policy. Since the policy is issued to you, you have the legal rights of a policy holder. You have the power to cancel the insurance, or replace it with another policy. You also have the responsibility to pay for the policy and manage all claims associated with the policy. Unless the insurer withdraws from doing business in your state, or withdraws the insurance product that you possess and offers a comparable replacement, you can keep your policy and your medical underwriting status as long as you pay for your policy on time and stay in your same location. An insurer withdrawing from a state is a big undertaking for the insurer and closely watched by the state department of insurance, so the likelihood of a good reason to withdraw is low for companies with a reasonable number of insureds.

> ☞ "Whether you buy individual or group depends on how healthy you are. Individual health insurance is based on your current and past health history. Group health insurance is guaranteed issue for a company smaller than 50. There might be tax advantages doing it through the company, there might be tax advantages doing it individually if you choose an HSA."
> -Dianne Lawton, Former Director of Individual Sales, John F. Sipp & Associates

An individual policy can be continued in force regardless of employment. When you move from one employer to another, your health insurance benefits do not change because your health insurance is not tied to your employment. If you were to get sick and be unable to work, you would not have to go through the difficulties associated with paying COBRA continuation of benefits and then trying to find a HIPAA guaranteed policy. However, the policy is not paid for by your employer, so this is money that comes out of your pocket. If you are self employed, or have a spouse who is, you can claim tax benefits for the cost of the insurance.

> ☞ **Annual Increases for Age**
> Commonly, when the last digit of your age changes to a five or a zero, your health insurance will have an additional increase, but the amount of the increase depends on the experience of the insurer. Individual policies may be the most open about this, since their rates tend to be published for all ages, and they can't be hidden inside groups. A quick check of some of the rates offered by Blue Cross Blue Shield of Rhode Island shows increases from 3% to 22%, lower for family plans, higher for single insureds.

One strong point is that in most states, medical underwriting of the policy is not allowed once the policy is in force and you keep it in force by paying and not moving out of the service area. This means that if you start out in excellent health when buying the policy, you cannot be moved to another, more expensive tier if you or a family member on the policy were to become significantly ill.

You should expect to see increases due to your increasing age and that of others on the policy, as well as annual inflationary increases due to the amount paid by the insurer for claims, but not increases specifically for you based on medical claims that you make.

+ / –	Point of Comparison – Individual Policy

+ / – **1. Medical Underwriting**

Medically underwritten in most states, generally those states that don't have community rating. It means lower rates for the healthier and higher rates, exclusions, or rejections for those with a medical condition.

– **2. Rate Caps**

No rate caps generally, though some states have laws on the books, many don't police this segment of the insurance industry as heavily as the employer group policies.

– **3. Guaranteed Issue**

Not guaranteed issue in most states. Check at www.BestHealthInsuranceBook.com, or check the table of the best states for those with a medical condition on page 32.

+ **4. Who Owns the Policy**

You own the policy.

+ / – **5. Does Rate Depend on Health**

The rate is likely to depend on health in most states. Check www.BestHealthInsuranceBook.com or the table of the best states for those with a medical condition on page 32. Good health will lead to lower rates in most states, those without community rating.

+ **6. When It Ends**

Ends when you cancel, don't pay, or the insurer withdraws from your state.

7. Who Pays

You pay.

+ **8. Annual Increases**

Annual increases likely to be level and in line with annual healthcare cost increases.

+ **9. Re-underwriting**

No re-underwriting after you start making claims.

– **10. Excluded Occupations**

Certain hard to insure professions may not be able to get coverage at all companies. You'll need to ask before applying. Occupations similar to or including the following may encounter some difficulties at certain insurers: air traffic controllers, toxic chemical workers (manufacturing and use, including crop dusters), divers, explosive workers, fishermen, oil well or refinery workers, sports professionals (including semi-pro), workers who work in the air at high heights (windows, roofing, or steel) or underground (miners), at high risk (soldiers, police, firefighters), or in stockyards, stables, or bars.

– **11. Existing Medical Conditions**

Medical conditions can mean a significantly higher rate or rejection.

+ **12. State of Regulation/State of Issue**

Regulated by your state, issued in your state.

+ **13. Difficulty in Getting Quotes**

Easy to get quotes, especially online.

– **14. Difficulty of Application**

Involved medical questionnaire when medical underwriting is involved.

– **15. Effect of Age on Rates**

Older age will lead to higher rates.

+ **16. Tax Benefits**

Tax benefits to the self employed or if you choose an HSA/HDHP.

+ / –	Point of Comparison – Individual Policy
+	17. **Annual Hassle** Little annual hassle – just pay the premiums.
–	18. **Conversion Options** Offers no "conversion" option except when the insurer ends sales of a plan and provides a replacement. You may not need a conversion if you get the right policy for your current and anticipated future needs.

Figure 6.1: Individual Policy Points of Comparison

Individual Purchase of Association Group Coverage

In many states it is possible to purchase individual coverage as part of an association group, which can include unions. However, this generally does not provide some of the benefits that people assume come with group health insurance, particularly a better rate and conversion options. In fact, you may experience large premium increases over the first few years, with the possibility that the group you sign up with will be cancelled if the group gets too small.

> ۞ Don't be confused. Association group coverage is not the same as employer group coverage. It does not have the same protections as employer group insurance, and is regulated by different laws.

This type of coverage is becoming more popular as people are looking for lower rates and insurers are simultaneously trying to find ways to meet market demand and underwrite people in groups. Unfortunately, association groups are not necessarily as long-lasting as employment groups. Because people can elect whether to be part of the association, unlike an employer where people have a lot more at stake (including a source of income), the healthier people tend to leave the association group when rates go up, leaving those with medical conditions and higher usage in the group, further raising the rates. This is a phenomenon common enough to have earned a name: the death spiral. Rates keep going up and the healthier people leave for less expensive options, until finally the group policy may be cancelled and your certificate of coverage is useless. This is particularly problematic for associations that do not have medical underwriting as part of the insurance application.

> ۞ **Problems Prevalent with Association Group Insurance:**
> 1. Low-balling makes the initial premium seem low or comparable with other plans, with significant hikes in rates after the first year.
> 2. Re-underwriting, while illegal in some states, may not be illegal everywhere, and may mean that after you have a claim that your rates shoot up.
> 3. Usual and customary amounts may be for another location that has significantly lower fees - meaning that you'll have to pay the difference if you go outside of a network or don't have a network.
> 4. Your agent may not tell you that you're buying association group coverage. Look for monthly fees or a membership fee in addition to the health insurance premium.
> 5. Limited benefits policies may be sold as "stacked" policies, appearing to have comprehensive benefits, but inspection of the fine print may reveal otherwise.
> 6. An out of state association may mean that neither your state or the state of the association will be able to help if you have a problem.
> 7. Out of state association coverage may not be regulated as strongly, or at all, in your state compared to in-state associations. Association coverage may not be regulated as strongly as individual coverage, whether in-state or out.

Your rate as part of an association group can depend on medical underwriting factors, unlike an employer group where everybody in the company who is covered pays the same amount. However, healthy people may leave the group over time, leaving only sick people in the group, which causes the rates to rise. The master policy is with the association, which may cancel or amend the policy without consulting you. You've only got a certificate of coverage, just like when you get health insurance through a group policy at work. If the policy is amended strongly to your disadvantage or cancelled, your only recourse is to find other insurance and terminate the coverage, and coverage is harder to get and more expensive if you have a medical condition.

If you are looking at getting insurance through an association, try to find one that is a bona-fide association that has a purpose and mission much stronger than just providing health insurance and other ancillary personal/business benefits. You are more likely to find this in long standing associations that have missions integral to certain industries or groups of people. You may already belong to such an association. For example, I have belonged to the Institute for Electrical and Electronics Engineers (IEEE) on and off since I was in college. This organization holds conferences, publishes papers and journals, and has a strong mission.

The IEEE has offered health insurance in the past. As of 2007 they closed the pool to new applicants, raised deductibles, and made many other significant changes. These changes included excluding certain members from the plan. These members were in essence kicked-out of the plan, and must find other insurance. They have HIPAA eligibility and they will pay the high HIPAA guaranteed rate unless they go through medical underwriting, which you may recall is beneficial for the young and healthy.

If you are still considering this type of insurance, perhaps because of the underwriting criteria of the insurer, such as allowing higher risk occupations, you may want to determine if you can obtain insurance from an in-state association rather than an out-of-state association. This subtle but important difference can mean the difference between having your state department of insurance there to back you up should any trouble occur versus a state of jurisdictional "limbo" where your state department of insurance and the association's state play tug of war over who represents you, if either of the groups are even able to help you.

+ / −		Point of Comparison – Association Group Coverage
+ / −	1.	**Medical Underwriting** Medically underwritten in most states which means lower rates for the healthier and higher rates, exclusions, or rejections for those with a medical condition.
−	2.	**Rate Caps** Generally no rate caps.
−	3.	**Guaranteed Issue** Not guaranteed issue in most states. Check using www.BestHealthInsuranceBook.com, or check the table of the best states for those with a medical condition on page 32.
−	4.	**Who Owns the Policy** The association owns the policy and can modify or cancel as they see fit.
+ / −	5.	**Does Rate Depend on Health** The rate is likely to depend on health in most states. Check www.BestHealthInsuranceBook.com or check the table of the best states for those with a medical condition on page 32. Good health will lead to lower rates for the first year.

+ / −		Point of Comparison – Association Group Coverage
−	6.	**When It Ends** Ends when you cancel, don't pay, the insurance company withdraws from state, or the insurance company withdraws the "block of business".
	7.	**Who Pays** You pay.
−	8.	**Annual Increases** Rates are likely to increase significantly after first anniversary.
−	9.	**Re-underwriting** Re-underwriting has occurred, and may occur in states where it is not yet illegal. Where legal, it is currently out of fashion to re-underwrite.
+	10.	**Excluded Occupations** May get coverage for harder to insure professions.
−	11.	**Existing Medical Conditions** Medical conditions can mean a significantly higher rate or rejection.
−	12.	**State of Regulation/State of Issue** Loosely regulated by your state, if at all, frequently issued in another state.
+	13.	**Difficulty in Getting Quotes** Easy to get quotes, especially online.
−	14.	**Difficulty of Application** Involved medical questionnaire, if medically underwritten.
−	15.	**Effect of Age on Rates** Older age will lead to higher rates.
+	16.	**Tax Benefits** Tax benefits to self employed or if you choose an HSA/HDHP.
+	17.	**Annual Hassle** Little annual hassle.
−	18.	**Conversion Options** Offers no conversion option, unlike employer group policies.

Figure 6.2: Association Group Points of Comparison

Individual Coverage as Part of an Employer Policy

This is the typical coverage that most people have obtained through an employer. The employer may pay a portion of the premium, and must have a certain percentage of employees participating in the plan. However, the employer can change the contribution that you make, change the plan, or even cancel the plan entirely, and you have no rights other than to find benefits and/or employment elsewhere.

This is health insurance that you are allowed to purchase as a benefit of being employed at a company. You may choose not to take this insurance, but it is often subsidized by the company. This can be considered a forced contribution to a group health insurance plan that you have not selected. There is also pressure on the employer

> **What Happens If Your Employer Closes?**
> If the employer goes out of business your health insurance or COBRA extension will be cancelled and you will have to look for other health insurance or go without.

from the insurers to enroll a certain percentage of employees, with waivers given for employees with insurance from spouses and those on Medicare. Employers consider health benefits to be part of your compensation. However, if you forego the health insurance your salary is unlikely to be adjusted.

Some of the more interesting aspects of this insurance is that it is guaranteed issue. This means that regardless of any medical conditions that you or a family member may have, you will be allowed to become part of the insurance policy. You may have to wait a certain number of months after obtaining employment, which may vary depending on whether you've had insurance just prior to your eligibility at the employer. You may also have a waiting period for any pre-existing condition, which again may depend on whether you've had health insurance just prior to becoming eligible at work.

The rate is also paid equally by all members of the group. The healthier people may pay a higher rate than if they bought insurance on their own. Those people with medical conditions may pay a lower rate than if they bought on their own, if they could even find any insurance for an insured's medical condition. This way of determining payment is basically "community rating", which is mandated in some states (with variation) for individual insurance. In some states, employers may offer a more limited package with lower rates.

Your insurance may end when employment ends, or you may extend it by paying everything that you and the employer pay, plus an additional few percent points for administration expenses. This extension, part of the COBRA law, typically runs 18 months for standard termination and longer for situations like disability. The costs may be high, but if you manage to pay until the end of the COBRA extension, you will be eligible

> Thinking about leaving your job? As far as health insurance goes, it's not a problem if you don't have any serious medical conditions. If you do have a serious medical condition, you'll want to consider moving to a spouse's plan, finding another job with benefits that don't have a waiting/exclusion period. If you can't do any of these, it'll cost you: take the COBRA for the 18 months, then get a HIPAA guaranteed plan.

to purchase HIPAA guaranteed insurance, though nobody is going to knock on your door to make sure you know about buying it. HIPAA guaranteed insurance can be even more expensive that your COBRA payment, but can be far less than you'd pay as someone with a medical condition.

Also, with employers cutting back on costs and benefits, the employer can scale back or cancel your health insurance at any time, and you've got no right to anything other than HIPAA portability, which is important if you've got a medical condition. Certainly you could find employment elsewhere, but then you've got job search time, plus a waiting period to get on the new employers plan, and any exclusions for pre-existing conditions to worry about, not to mention a new employer, possibly in a new location.

+ / −	Point of Comparison – Employer's Group
+	1. **Medical Underwriting** Not individually medically underwritten. The group members as a whole (or the initial set of insureds) may have some medical underwriting.
+	2. **Rate Caps** Rate increases tend to be capped by the state more aggressively than other types of insurance.

+ / –		Point of Comparison – Employer's Group

+   3. **Guaranteed Issue**
Guaranteed issue to individuals in the group, but groups can have difficulty finding affordable policies depending on health status or occupation.

–   4. **Who Owns the Policy**
The employer owns the policy and can do as they wish, including changing or cancelling the policy.

+ / –   5. **Does Rate Depend on Health**
The rate depends on the contribution of employer and health history of employees past and present. Good health doesn't lower the rate as directly as an individual plan does.

–   6. **When It Ends**
Ends when you leave employment, with typically an 18 month extension for companies of 20 or more people. Can also end abruptly when the employer decides not to offer health insurance or goes out of business.

      7. **Who Pays**
You may pay a portion, and the employer pays a portion. You might consider that it is really your money that the employer is spending, they're just paying you less.

–   8. **Annual Increases**
Rates can go anywhere depending on the health expenditures of the group and changes the employer may make in the plan, though it tends to be capped as in (2) above.

+   9. **Re-underwriting**
Re-underwriting of individuals will not happen. An experience rating for the group will affect rates. The more claims that happen, the higher the rate.

–   10. **Excluded Occupations**
Certain types of business may have high rates, see a higher increase annually, and might drop the plan if the increase is too large.

+   11. **Existing Medical Conditions**
Your medical conditions and utilization will be spread across the premiums paid for the entire group.

+   12. **State of Regulation/State of Issue**
Regulated by the state, except for large groups and other groups who are self insured and regulated by federal law.

+   13. **Difficulty in Getting Quotes**
Really easy quotes: the employer tells you your choices and the rates, though your choices may be severely limited.

+   14. **Difficulty of Application**
No medical questionnaire.

      15. **Effect of Age on Rates**
Older age will lead to higher rates for the group, but not any one individual.

+   16. **Tax Benefits**
Tax benefits to the employer and to you because the contribution to the health insurance is not taxed.

+   17. **Annual Hassle**
Little annual hassle, just make choices during the annual "open season."

+   18. **Conversion Options**
Conversion options to individual policies when leaving company, but HIPAA guaranteed policies may be noticeably more expensive.

Figure 6.3: Employer's Group Points of Comparison

Group Coverage at Your Own Company

If you have a company of your own, or are self employed, then you may be eligible to purchase a group health insurance policy for your business. Some states allow you to purchase a group policy for a single person, some require a group of at least two. In fact, some states require insurers to offer some basic health insurance policies to the small group of one or two (depending on state law) to about 50 employees as a condition of selling insurance in the state. Rules vary by state and are always changing, so you'll need to check to see which apply to you.

As the boss of your own company (incorporated, LLC, partnership, sole proprietor, or a similar business entity), you are engaged in some sort of legitimate business pursuit. You, through your company, are eligible for group insurance. A company with the sole purpose of getting health insurance probably won't fly. It has to be an ongoing business concern. Hobbies that are turned into a business (like selling quilts at craft fairs) would probably work, but you'd need to make enough money with these ventures to pay the expenses of the company plus those of health insurance.

This type of insurance will be guaranteed issue. For example, North Carolina has two model plans that must be offered by any insurer in the state to a business group. If your group members (employees and families) are reasonably healthy, then rates will be better. However, these group rates, with guaranteed issue, tend to be higher than individual rates. Group health for one or more household members may cost more or less than individual. Several combinations of coverage might be considered.

> "If a person has a corporation, a business plan of one is possible. The insurer can't rate you up in a small group as much as an individual plan, so if you have a medical condition it is better to get a company group plan."
> -Beth B. Parrott, Owner, Parrott Insurance and Benefits

To set up a group, you'll need to work through a health insurance agent. You can't just do it online or by simply sending in an application. There are also annual audits, fees, and other paperwork and expenses associated with having this type of a plan. However the hassles may be worth it. It may be the best choice for some people: those who cannot find affordable insurance due to health or other concerns. If you get some young healthy people working at your company, they can offset the expense of those with a medical condition.

Since your company owns the policy, you'll be the one calling the shots. You can modify benefits and make changes to the deductibles and type of plan prior to the annual renewal. You can choose to have more benefits, or fewer benefits, than individual insurance offers. However, you'll also have more work to do since renewal increases are inevitable and you may have to work harder to make a switch, especially if you add employees over time. You'll have annual paperwork to complete, which you can't easily hand over to an outside professional. In fact, for some the overhead associated with a company and employees can grow to be a big burden, which drives another industry: the employee leasing business. However, if you go that route, you lose control over the health insurance which can lead to difficulties as the employee leasing industry matures.

+/–		Point of Comparison – Your Own Company Group
+ / –	1.	**Medical Underwriting** The rate is medically underwritten for small groups (under approximately 51 lives), but not for any one individual.
+	2.	**Rate Caps** Rate increases can be more limited and subject to more oversight.
+	3.	**Guaranteed Issue** Guaranteed issue in most states for individuals on the plan, though certain lines of work may make it expensive or nearly impossible to obtain for a group.
+	4.	**Who Owns the Policy** Employer owns the policy, but if you own the business it's you.
	5.	**Does Rate Depend on Health** The rate depends on the contribution by employer and health history of employees past and present. Good health will lower the overall rate and more directly benefit you as the group may be smaller and healthier.
+	6.	**When It Ends** Ends when you leave employment, with typically an 18 month extension for companies of 20 or more people. It can end abruptly when you (the employer) decide not to offer health insurance or you close the company. It can also end if you (the employer/owner) sell the business.
+	7.	**Who Pays** You (the employer) decide the portion that the company pays and the employees pay, within the limits of the law and the policy.
	8.	**Annual Increases** Rates can go anywhere depending on the health expenditures of the group and changes you (the employer) may make in the plan, within the limits set by the law in your state.
+	9.	**Re-underwriting** Re-underwriting of individuals will not happen, but for the group as a whole, the rate will change based on claims made. By law, you cannot discriminate in hiring based on the health of the employee. The claims paid to those insured in the group will affect the rates.
	10.	**Excluded Occupations** Certain types of businesses may see a higher initial rate, and/or higher annual increases.
+	11.	**Existing Medical Conditions** Your medical conditions and utilization will be spread across the premiums paid for the entire group.
+	12.	**State of Regulation/State of Issue** Regulated by the state of the employer.
–	13.	**Difficulty in Getting Quotes** Significant effort to assemble quotes and options.
–	14.	**Difficulty of Application** The might be a medical questionnaire for each of the initial insured persons, with plenty of other paperwork.

+/−	Point of Comparison – Your Own Company Group

15. **Effect of Age on Rates**
Older age will lead to higher rates for the group, but not the individual. The share of the premium is divided evenly among the members of the group: young, old, sick, or healthy, all have the same contribution.

+ 16. **Tax Benefits**
Tax benefits to you (the employer) and to you (the individual) because the contribution to the health insurance is not taxed.

− 17. **Annual Hassle**
Noticeable annual hassles. Copies of tax forms, benefit meetings if you have other employees, and rate increases may mean that you shop for another plan or insurer.

+ 18. **Conversion Options**
Conversion options to individual policies when leaving the company, but HIPAA guaranteed policies may be noticeably more expensive.

Figure 6.4: Your Own Company Group Points of Comparison

Summary

Summary of Individual vs. Group for Individuals/Families with Health Issues

Point of Comparison	Individual Policy	Association Group	Employer Group	Your Company Group
1. Medical Underwriting	+ / −	+ / −	+	+ / −
2. Rate Caps	−	−	+	+
3. Guaranteed Issue	−	−	+	+
4. Who Owns the Policy	+	−	−	+
5. Rate Depends on Health	+ / −	+ / −	+ / −	
6. When It Ends	+	−	−	+
7. Who Pays				+
8. Annual Increases	+	−	−	
9. Re-underwriting	+	−	+	+
10. Excluded Occupations	−	+	−	
11. Existing Medical Conditions	−	−	+	+
12. State of Regulation/State of Issue	+	−	+	+
13. Difficulty in Getting Quotes	+	+	+	−
14. Difficulty of Application	−	−	+	−
15. Effect of Age on Rates	−			
16. Tax Benefits	+	+	+	+
17. Annual Hassle	+	+	+	−
18. Conversion Options	−	−	+	+

Figure 6.5: Summary of Points of Comparison for Ways of Getting Health Insurance

There are many pros and cons to each of the type of health insurance. Your needs and desires will be unique compared those of other people. The summary table should help you to determine which of the types of health insurance is best for you. I certainly found out a lot, having had employer group insurance, association group, and individual policies in the past, and seriously looking at the small group option. I consider an individual policy my first choice, followed by my own company group. But at my last job, I would have had a hard time saying no to the employer group – it was fully paid by the employer. When I had an association group plan, I sometimes worried at night about it. I only had a certificate of coverage, and had never seen the master policy, which I would have had to travel to another state to view.

When you figure out which type suits you best, second best, and which you should not consider, you can use that to narrow the list of insurers that you will obtain from your state in Chapter 7.

Chapter 7

Your List of Insurers

The surest way to buy legitimate insurance and prevent a rip-off is to start with a list of licensed insurers in your state. Bona-fide insurance companies that wish to do business in a state must make filings with the state agency responsible for insurance. This takes a lot of time and effort on the part of the insurer, so it means that the insurer is serious and not a fly-by-night operation. To help you get the current list for your state, telephone numbers and links to your state department of insurance can be found in Appendix B and at www.BestHealthInsuranceBook.com

There are usually two lists of interest: one for individuals who are buying their own insurance, and the other list for companies that are buying employee group insurance. You know from the last chapter whether individual or group insurance is appropriate for you. You'll need to get a list of insurers from your state and narrow the list using financial information, quality, number insured in your area, and features offered by insurers. You'll end up with your own "short list" of insurers that you'll use in the next chapters. Be sure that when you look at the list of insurers selling to individuals that you make note of those that are selling "group association" coverage, since it is different than individual insurance.

Get Your List of Health Insurers from Your State

Having a list of individual or small group insurers in hand is a good way to get started. You'll have the complete list of insurers licensed in your state. That way when you find agents, you'll know which companies the agent will be able to represent. You can buy insurance directly from some companies using their in-house agents, or their websites. Insurers will also be able to provide a list of agents in your area whom they have authorized to sell their products. All transactions will have an agent listed on them, someone who is licensed in your state. You should check on any agents with your state department of insurance.

Check Appendix B or www.BestHealthInsuranceBook.com for where to get lists. Some states have websites with lists which are given directly as URLs. Some states have separate lists of HMOs versus other Health Insurance. Many states combine Health with Life, so lists of just Health Insurers are harder to get online. Call your state department of insurance for the list and get it over the phone, or they might mail, fax, or email the list to

> For Medicare shoppers, there is a national database of all insurers. Go to www.medicare.com or call 1-800-MEDICARE to get lists for Medigap, Medicare Advantage (Part C), Prescription (Part D), and Medicare Savings Accounts.

you. Some publications, such as local newspapers, will print a list of the top insurers in your area. Certainly the top insurers are worth considering. However, don't assume that the top selling plan at any insurer is the right one for you. Find the features that you need, and do the financial comparison in Chapter 8 to determine which works best for you.

What about finding other insurers/plans not regulated by your state? Most are eventually proven to be illegal or scams. It is best to stick with the list of licensed insurers provided by your state. As an example, take a look at the list on the next page from the North Carolina Department of Insurance Website.

Licensed Insurers Marketing Individual Health Insurance Coverage in North Carolina
NC Department of Insurance

The following insurers are actively marketing individual health insurance coverage, typically termed major medical insurance, in the State of North Carolina according to the Department's records. This list is periodically reviewed and updated if needed, but may not reflect recent changes in a company's status.

Current as of 05/29/2007

Licensed Name	Address	Phone Number	Comments
Aetna Life Insurance Company	PO Box 730 Blue Bell, PA 19422	(800) MY Health (800) 694-3258	
American Medical Security Life Insurance Company	P.O. Box 19032 Green Bay, WI 54307	(414) 226-6300 (800) 452-4250	Association group coverage *
American National Insurance Company	One Moody Plaza, 8th Floor Galveston, TX 77550	800-899-6502	
American Republic Insurance Company	P.O. Box 1 Des Moines, IA 50310	(515) 245-2000 (800) 247-2190	Association group coverage *
Blue Cross Blue Shield of North Carolina	P.O. Box 2291 Durham, NC 27702	(800) 324-4973	
Celtic Insurance Company	200 S. Wacker Drive Chicago, IL 60606	(800) 284-0060	
Continental General Insurance Company	P.O. Box 247007 Omaha, NE 68124-7007	(402) 397-3200	Association group coverage *
Golden Rule Insurance Company	7440 Woodland Dr. Indianapolis, IN 46278-1719	(800) 444-8990	Association group coverage *
Guarantee Trust Life Insurance Company	1275 Milwuakee Avenue Glenview, IL 60025	(800) 338-7452	
Humana Insurance Company	500 W. Main Street Louisville, KY 40202	(800) 664-4140	
John Alden Life Insurance Company	P.O. Box 3050 Milwaukee, WI 53201-3050	(800) 800-1212	Association group coverage *

* Coverage is limited to members of associations to whom the group master policy is issued.

Figure 7.1: Licensed Individual Health Insurers – State of North Carolina

Licensed Insurers Marketing Individual Health Insurance Coverage in North Carolina
NC Department of Insurance

The following insurers are actively marketing individual health insurance coverage, typically termed major medical insurance, in the State of North Carolina according to the Department's records. This list is periodically reviewed and updated if needed, but may not reflect recent changes in a company's status.

Current as of 05/29/2007

Licensed Name	Address	Phone Number	Comments
Mega Life and Health Insurance Company	9151 Boulevard 26 North Richaland Hills, TX 76180	813-586-8733	Association group coverage*
Mid-West National Life Insurance Company of Tennessee	4001 McEwen Drive Dallas, TX 75244	(800) 767-0700	Association group coverage *
National Foundation Life Insurance Company	801 Cherry St., Unit 33 FT Worth, TX 76102	(800) 221-9039	
Reserve National Insurance Company	6100 N.W. Grand Blvd., Oklahoma City, OK 73118	(800)-654-9106	
Time Insurance Company	501 West Michigan Avenue Milwaukee, WI 53201	(800) 800-1212	Association group coverage *
United American Insurance Company	2700 S. Stonebridge Dr. McKinney, TS 75070	(214)-320-6722	
United HealthCare Insurance Company	AARP Division, PO Box 130 Montgomery, PA 18936	(866) 270-8022 (Telephone # is for AARP Personal Health Insurance Plans)	Association group coverage *
WellPath Select, Inc.	2801 Slater Rd., Suite 200 Morrisville, NC 27560	(866) 364-5663	Individual HMO
World Insurance Company	P.O. Box 3160 Omaha, NE 68103-0160	(402) 496-8000 (800) 786-7557	Association group coverage *

* Coverage is limited to members of associations to whom the group master policy is issued.

Figure 7.1 gives the names of the insurers for individual insurance. There is a separate list for insurers offering small group insurance to employers. Frequently all insurers selling employer group insurance have to offer small business group plans, and in North Carolina there are a minimum of two plans that must be offered to all small businesses.

Check the table on page 87 to see which insurers on the list are actually part of the same parent company. This will help you to group your quotes together. Contact information on the list can be useful, though this list does not include the web site URLs. Some companies will provide rates and information directly on their website: an open approach to providing information. Other companies will not provide anything but basic information on their website, preferring more control about how they disseminate information.

The comments column is very interesting. When I called the state department of insurance to ask what association group coverage was, they said that it was an out-of-state association and that they couldn't help much further, including if there was a problem. You already understand the association group coverage information, having read Chapter 6. Not all states provide information about which insurers sell association group coverage. You'll need to figure that out yourself or get help from an agent.

Now that you've got a list of insurers (individual and/or group), you can begin to narrow down the list to those insurers that are a fit for you.

Narrowing the List

In the previous chapter, you narrowed the list initially by determining which of the four types of insurance you would consider (individual, association group, employer group, your small business group). Now you need to narrow the list further to determine how comfortable you are with each insurer. If you work with an independent agent, you will get valuable advice about how certain insurers work with their policyholders. You can couple that advice with your own homework by using the criteria of financial health, quality, size, and features to come up with a reasonable short list.

> **Insurers: For Profit, Non-Profit, Mutual Company, does it matter?**
> In many ways, there are no differences. But when it comes to the list of who's most important, here's how it looks:
> - For Profit: Stockholders
> - Non-Profit: The Mission
> - Mutual: The Policyholders

Financial Status of Health Insurers

Before buying a policy with any company you'll want to check on the financial health of your insurer. You can do this quickly, easily, and at no cost from a website such as:

- www.moodys.com
- www.ambest.com
- www.standardandpoors.com
- www.fitchibca.com
- or for a fee at www.weissratings.com

The rating services use different grades, such as AAA or A++ for the top grade, so check the ratings structure for any site that you use. You need to know the place of your insurer to the industry as a whole. Currently the health insurance industry top score is around B+. You can also find information such as this from your local library. Ask at the reference desk.

Quality of Health Plans

In addition to information provided by insurers about their health plans, some third party information is available that may help you to determine which plan is right for you. This includes complaint statistics from your state department of insurance, review and commentary by consumer and industry organizations, and news stories about specific insurers. The information is not usually reported about specific plans, but rather about a company as a whole, and people will have different levels of satisfaction with different plans offered by the same company. But knowing

> Internet websites and blogs can be very useful to find out problems that other people have had. But be careful not to scare yourself when reading remarks about your plan from unknown sources. Competitors may disparage each other anonymously online, and you may end up finding little more than gossip from unverified sources.

how well a company rates overall should help you to determine if the insurer is right for you.

Your state department of insurance is your advocate when having problems with an insurer. The department also keeps track of each of these complaints and the outcome. So when choosing an insurer, checking the information available from the state department of insurance will help you to determine if prospective insurers are right for you. This can be done by checking with the state department of insurance directly, or through the website of the National Association of Insurance Commissioners (NAIC).

In North Carolina, statistics are posted to the state website periodically. Information can also be obtained by calling the consumer assistance hotline. I have tried both approaches and found that you can get basic information on a large number of insurers more effectively through the website, and more detailed, specific information about a single insurer through the hotline.

The complaint information is provided in the form of ratios. This is the number of complaints divided by the number of insured people. So a company having five complaints with a thousand insureds has a much higher ratio (0.005) than a company with fifty complaints and a million insured people (0.00005). The ratios may be provided separately for group versus individual plans. You can check both even though you may be looking for individual coverage. This is because some insurance sold to individuals may actually be group insurance provided to a group, such as an association (check the fine print). Human error or lack of clarity about whether a policy is an individual or a group may also incorrectly classify a complaint. Plus, regardless of group or individual, it is still the same company that you are choosing as an insurer.

Consumer Reports, the magazine of Consumers Union, provides satisfaction information about insurers based on member surveys. The frequency of the updates to this information depends on the editorial calendar of the magazine. At the time of writing, the most recent update is September 2007. It is available from libraries if you do not subscribe to the magazine. You can also access this information on the internet through their website (www.ConsumerReports.org) for which access fees are charged for much of the content. J.D. Power, the consumer rating company famous for the satisfaction survey of automobiles, also rates health insurance companies. Search at www.jdpower.com.

Industry groups also provide information about the quality of the health insurers. The National Association of Insurance Commissioners (www.naic.org) has a consumer section on its website. You can get information that is similar to that provided by your state insurance division, although the numbers may not be exactly the same due to the way the data is collected and updated. I found that the reports provided by NAIC had a lot more detail in the categories of the complaints than the state reports. You can see more specifically the complaints and their resolutions. You have to read through and make sense of some of the categories to figure out how important each of the criteria is to your decision.

The National Committee for Quality Assurance (NCQA) (www.ncqa.org) provides a report card of managed care providers (HMO, PPO) based on your state and location. Many of the managed care plans in the nation participate. There is information about the quality of treatment for specific conditions, as well as overall information for plans listed for a company. If the plan that you are considering is not listed, infer what you can from the other plans at the same company.

Gather all of this information for the most recent year and prior years. Shorten your list of insurers as you learn more. Once you've narrowed down your insurer list, looking at trends will help you further. Obviously companies with declining complaint ratios and improving quality and financial scores are better. How the company moves in comparison to the other health insurers is an important way to compare companies. When I was researching my options, the financial health of the insurers was slightly declining across the industry. A company that rates as well as the industry or better was a good choice for me.

News sources are important knowing about happenings with insurance companies. You don't need to read the paper every day and remember everything about every insurer in order to figure out important information about your prospective insurers. You can go to the library and get assistance in searching for information about specific companies or health insurance in general for your state. You can also use online services provided by libraries, news organizations, or subscription news databases. Information of interest includes new offerings, lawsuits, mergers, and other stories about the insurers. For example, there was a lawsuit in Florida regarding the re-underwriting of customers who had a major medical event and the subsequent raising of premiums for those people. This was reported by major newspapers including the Wall Street Journal, and included the settlement information: this insurer claimed that it had not done anything illegal with this practice, but would refrain from re-underwriting in Florida (for now). This helped me to understand how this insurer, and others who were not caught, could raise rates in Florida, and how legislation elsewhere would prevent this type of rate increase. Another example of useful news that personally helped me was the merger information about who was acquired by who. The additional statements that the companies that were acquired would be brought up to the quality standards of the acquiring company allowed me to consider these insurers.

Many Names, Same Company

Sometimes a company will be branded all under the same name which makes it easy to know whom you are dealing with. Sometimes companies are assembled from mergers and acquisitions and the choice is made to keep the existing names. Regardless of the reason, it is advantageous to you, the consumer, to know the different names that a company is using. For example, in an acquisition scenario, a company with a checkered past may be in a quality upswing when acquired by a company with a strong quality ethic. In another case,

ⓠ **Examples of Simple Names**

**Blue Cross Blue Shield
of North Carolina**
(an independent company -
like many)

Cigna Corporation
Cigna Healthcare (& variations)

Humana, Inc.
Humana (& variations)

ⓠ **Examples of Complex Names**

Aetna Inc.
Aetna Health (& variations)
Aetna U.S. Healthcare
United States Health Care
Systems of Pennsylvania

American Enterprise
American Republic
National Consumer Alliance
Association
World Insurance

American National
National Business Association
InterNational Consumers
Alliance

Assurant Health
AlumniMed / GradMed
(underwritten by Assurant)
American Health Resources
Association
Fortis Insurance
Health Advocates Alliance
John Alden Life Insurance
Time Insurance
Union Security Insurance

Centene Corporation
Managed Health Services
University Health Plans Inc.
Buckeye Community Health
Plan
Superior Health Plan
Peach State Health Plan

Coventry Health Care, Inc.
Carelink Health Plans Inc.
Coventry Health Care (&
variations)
Group Health Plan Inc.
HealthAmerica

HealthCare USA
OmniCare Health Plan
Southern Health Services
Wellpath Community Health
Plans

**Health Care Service
Corporation**
Blue Cross and Blue Shield of
Oklahoma
Blue Cross and Blue Shield of
Texas

Health Net Inc.
FHS Life & Health (Foundation
Health Systems)
Health Net (& variations)

HealthMarkets
Alliance for Afforable Health
Care
Alliance for Affordable Services
American Society of Women
Entrepreneurs
Americans for Financial Security
MEGA Life and Health Insurance
Company
Mid-West National Life
Insurance Company of
Tennessee
National Association for the Self
Employed (NASE)

Highmark
Highmark Blue Cross Blue Shield
Highmark Blue Shield
Mountain State Blue Cross Blue
Shield
Keystone Health Plan West

HIP Holdings
Health Insurance Plan (HIP)
Health Plan of New York
Vytra Health Plans
ConnectiCare
PerfectHealth
Group Health Inc. (GHI)

**Kaiser Foundation Health Plan
Inc.**
Kaiser Foundation Health Plan
(& variations)
Kaiser Permanente
Southern California Permanente
Medical Group

Sierra Health Services
Health Plan of Nevada Inc.
Sierra Health and Life Insurance
Company

**UnitedHealth Group
Incorporated**
American Medical Security
Group Inc.
AmeriChoice Corporation
Golden Rule Insurance
Company
Federation of American
Consumers and Travelers
(FACT)
Mid Atlantic Medical Services,
Inc.
Midwest Security Insurance
Companies
Oxford Health Plans
Pacificare (and variations)
Taxpayers Network Inc. (TNI)
United HealthCare (& variations)

Wellpoint Inc.
Anthem Health Plans (variations)
Anthem Blue Cross Blue Shield
Blue Cross Blue Shield of
Georgia
Blue Cross Blue Shield of
Missouri
Blue Cross Blue Shield of
Wisconsin
Blue Cross of California
Community Insurance Company
Compcare Health Services
Insurance Corporation
Empire Blue Cross Blue Shield
Empire HealthChoice
Health Alliance Life Insurance
Company
HealthKeepers Inc.
Healthlink
HMO Missouri
Lumenos
Peninsula Health Care Inc.
Priority Health Care Inc.
RightCHOICE Managed Care
Inc.
Rocky Mountain Hospital and
Medical Service
WellChoice New Jersey

Figure 7.2: Many Names, Same Company

you may benefit to know that quotes from seemingly different companies are from the same company. When tracking news stories, it may help to keep track of the white hats and the black hats.

Figure 7.2 provides the ownership hierarchy of many of the largest health insurers throughout the United States. Blue Cross and Blue Shield are individual licensees of the Blue Cross Blue Shield Association, so they're not related unless owned by the same company. They are just both members of the same association and they may have similar national networks. You may be able to use North Carolina Blue Cross Blue Shield at most of the providers that accept Blue Cross Blue Shield regardless of whether you're in the Anthem or the North Carolina Blue Cross Blue Shield areas.

Why You Shouldn't Ask Your Friends

Unless your friends are professionals in health insurance, their impressions of their plan may depend on their experience with a certain doctor, or an unexpected hospitalization where they were responsible for a deductible. Most of us don't eat, sleep, and breathe health insurance information, and each person's search for insurance is unique and different. However, finding that an insurer doesn't pay claims for reasonable services may be useful, so be sure to carefully listen to the reasons if you are discussing this topic with friends.

Number Covered in State / Number Covered in Area

The number of people (or "lives" as some refer to it) covered is a secondary factor that has some importance. You want to make sure that the policy will continue to be in force when you need it, and not be withdrawn in your state. An insurer can leave a state if the pool of insureds is too small and unprofitable, as many Medicare HMO's have done. That would leave you without insurance after a period of time, and without any easy way to move to another insurer, especially if you have gotten sick.

You also want to make sure that the number insured in your local area (county, group of counties, or metropolitan area) is not minimal. You want to make sure that the network that you use, if you've chosen one, is large enough and has enough people, doctors and facilities to make it viable for the long term. You don't want to face the problem of an insurer pulling out of the state or your area of the state.

Features

Finally, you need to make sure that the features that you want from Chapter 4 are included in the list of insurers. If you've got your heart set on a PPO plan, and none make the list from the previous eliminations in this chapter, then you'll either have to include some plans that you eliminated or choose something other than a PPO.

> ☼ Why not get every feature? Because every feature that you buy costs you money. Buying unnecessary features means that you are spending money on something that you are less likely to use – and that is not your best deal.

Summary

Now you've got a list of licensed insurers in your state that you have narrowed by quality factors. Now it's time to get some quotes and do a financial comparison, the topic of the next chapter.

Chapter 8

Financial Comparison

If you're like me, when you see the array of numbers presented by each health insurance plan, you feel overwhelmed and just want to "pick one". However, I've learned that this strategy has not always served me well. I've seen friends and family do much better with their choices than I have. So I developed a technique to take the most important numbers and come out with a cost for having each plan, for both a healthy year and also a year when one or more family members has a significant medical event, such as a broken arm or worse. By looking at these two numbers across all health plans, you will be able to choose the right plan for you.

I also think about what happens when I reach the age for Medicare to kick in, and how the amount spent on health insurance would hopefully go down for me, assuming we've got some kind of senior health system when I retire. I also know that as my children grow older and move out, they'll be getting their own health insurance, since they cannot continue on my policy past a certain age, as defined by the policy and the laws of my state.

> "You need to know the worst case - going in - and compare it to the best case."
> *-Jennifer McLaurin, Director of Sales, John F. Sipp & Associates*

Do you worry that the rates will be going up? One trick that financial professionals use to manage this worry is to use "constant dollars". This means that while the rates will go up in an inflationary manner, a certain percentage each year, they will move in a way that the rest of the financial markets move – generally in a predictable upward curve, but not predictable enough to know exactly how much. Using constant dollars allows you to look at the health expenses in today's dollars, and make your choice based on that information. Since you are comparing only between health plans, the amount that the insurance will go up each year should be reasonably close among well managed health insurance plans of the same type (individual, association, employer).

Of course, with all these numbers to manage, having a computer with a spreadsheet program is very helpful. However, the calculations are very simple, and anyone with a calculator can do them. But if you obtain many quotes, then you'll need to do the calculations for each quote, and this can take a little time. Check out the book website at www.BestHealthInsuranceBook.com for downloads and online tools to make the process easier.

Whose Pocket?

One important thing to understand about the quotes is that as the deductible goes up, your monthly payment goes down. If you look at the numbers that you will assemble during your quote gathering process, you will notice that there is variance across companies about how much a month you will pay versus how high the deductibles and coinsurance run. You will also notice that with a higher deductible and coinsurance amount, the lower your monthly payment will go. If you are able to save the money each month, then you can invest the difference in monthly premiums, and you may come out ahead in as little as a year. However, if you are not likely to invest the difference, then you may consider a lower deductible, and let the insurance company "invest" the difference for you, though they are going to pay expenses and claims with it. If you ever leave the insurer, you'll forfeit any amount that they might have "invested" on your behalf.

It's good to consider a high deductible plan and invest the rest, so that you keep the savings with you. The biggest downside to this is that you will have to shoulder the burden in the event that you must pay the deductible/coinsurance on the health insurance plan year after year – if, of course you keep the same plan year after year. Whether

> ⌾ "With the HSA beneficiary you can leave money to your children, so if there's money still in the account, it can be left behind."
> -Jennifer McLaurin, Director of Sales, John F. Sipp & Associates

you have an HSA, which affords savings on taxes, or just save and invest the savings on your premiums, you'll have those funds available for your use in the future.

Gather Rate Quotes

Rates quoted are the rate that most subscribers are likely to get, and are good until a certain date. If there is no medical underwriting, then it is the rate that you will actually get. With

medical underwriting there is a slight chance that your rate will be lower if you are in better health than the majority of people. If medically underwritten, there is also a chance that if your health is less than good, that your rate could be higher. Your best bet is to check with your agent who will have experience with any conditions that you might have, and how the different insurers may rate those conditions.

> ⌾ "All quotes from an insurer are exactly the same regardless of where you get them. The difference is that we provide the service."
> -Beth B. Parrott, Owner, Parrott Insurance and Benefits

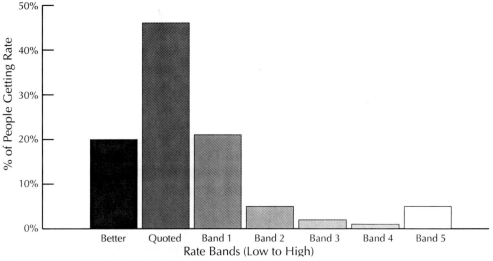

Figure 8.1: Example of Rate Tiers.

Referring to Figure 8.1, you can see that an insurer will quote the rate that most people get: "Quoted". Some folks, who are in optimal health, will get the "Better" rate, which can be even lower that the quoted rate. However, other people, due to health concerns, are likely to get rates that are higher than the quoted rate. In North Carolina the rate can be as high as seven times the quoted rate for the highest risk policies. Paying the premium can be difficult for some people. Keep in mind that the premium may be high, but medical bills could possibly be higher without coverage.

The quoted rates are for the first year. The companies are not required, and in fact don't provide any rates for second and subsequent years. They can't know how cost increases will drive rates up and how utilization of the policies will also cause rates to go up to pay for all the claims. However, if your state provides open access to most insurance company filings, you can find out interesting bits of information, including

> If the premium for a similar deductible/coinsurance/copay is much lower for one plan, look in the small print for a disclaimer about how the policy is not a substitute for comprehensive medical insurance, and don't buy it.

rate increases for insurers. An extreme example of this is an insurer, which sells an out of state association plan, that provides information about how they would automatically increase the rate by 10% after the first year, on top of the annual increases due to utilization and cost increases. This rate increase could be appealed, though I wonder if they tell their customers this. I could not find it in the certificate of coverage issued by the company to me. It could be appealed only if there were no claims. This would be an unpleasant surprise.

Getting Internet Quotes

The Internet has created incredible opportunities for information gathering and tremendous consumer advantages. But it has also given rise to much misinformation, and new pitfalls that can ensnare even the savviest consumer.

The best part of getting quotes from a website is that you can get many, many quotes. The bad part is that you are on your own to try to understand them and the subtle differences that can make a big difference to you. Unless you are completely 100% healthy and understand the products thoroughly, applying for insurance online can be a risky. You may be denied or given a higher rate than quoted. Or the plan you buy won't work for you down the road should you develop a serious medical condition.

Use the Internet to gather information. Consider your health and how well you understand the process and questions. Then make your choice as to whether you are a good candidate to apply for health insurance online. I've done it both ways: online and with an agent. There is no substitute for personal guidance and review of the forms from someone that you know and trust before submitting an application. However, if you cannot find someone you trust to work with you, or need something fast, then the Internet is a good choice. Since even online you are dealing with an insurance agent, most likely an independent one, you can contact them via email, chat, or telephone for answers to your questions.

There used to be a number of different websites offering online quotes, but there has been an incredible consolidation as one of the largest sites, eHealthInsurance.com has become the technology source for many different insurance agencies. For example, it used to be that you'd go to one of many sites, and get a different experience and different quotes. But the consolidation has led to a number of companies using the best technology to deliver their health insurance products to you.

Since there is so much change underway in the internet marketplace, the best place to find online quotes is to go to www.BestHealthInsuranceBook.com in the health insurance section. Also remember that no one site is likely to offer insurance from all the insurers in your state. You may need to visit a number to gather all of your information.

There are four kinds of sites:

1. A website for a single insurer that provides information and quotes for that insurer. In some cases, this may be the only way to get online quotes from a particular insurer because they may not participate in any of the online health insurance shopping malls. An example of this is www.bcbsnc.com – Blue Cross Blue Shield of North Carolina.

2. A website that gives quotes and policy information from a number of insurers immediately without entering any contact information:

- www.ehealthinsurance.com – market leader for internet sales of health insurance

- www.extendbenefits.com – used by Sam's Club for health insurance sales

3. A website that takes contact information and gives quotes immediately with a follow-up from an agent likely. An example of this is www.hsafinder.com which provides HSA information and quotes from agents.

4. A website that takes contact information and then quotes are given after one or more agents contact you:

- www.netquote.com

- www.insure.com

The first type may provide the most detailed information from the provider but not necessarily in a standard form across insurers. The second type really gives you a lot of control to find out information anonymously. The third type is nearly as good at basic information,

Your Annual Estimates				
Number of Wellness Office Visits	5	Well Visit Labs	$100	Est Prescripti
Number of Sick Office Visits	15	Sick Visit Labs	$0	Est HSA allow
Annual Number of Office Visits	20	Est. Lab Costs:	$100	

Office Visit $55.00

						Wellness				Prescriptions		Deductible			Coinsurance		Your Responsibility		
Company	Plan	Network	HSA/H DHP	Type: Individ Assoc, Empl	Labs Inclu ded?	Office Visit Copay	Well Office Visit Copay	Well Labs Y/N	Y/N	Scrip Deductible	Scrip Max	Individual	Family Max #	Family	%	Limit	Indiv Max	Fam. Max #	Fam
A	H	A	Y	I	N	$55	$0	Y	Y		$2,000	$5,450	1	$5,450	50%	$4,550	$2,275	1	$2
G	HSA		Y	A	N	$100	$100	N	N			$5,500	1	$5,500	100%	$0	$0	1	
A	H	A	Y	I	N	$55	$0	Y	Y		$2,000	$10,000	1	$10,000	100%	$0	$0	1	
G	O	GC	N	A	Y	$30	$30	Y	N			$2,500	2	$5,000	50%	$8,000	$4,000	2	$8
I	HSA		Y	A	N	$100	$100	N	N			$10,500	1	$10,500	0%	$0	$0	1	
J	HSA		Y	A	N	$100	$100	N	N			$5,450	1	$5,450	0%	$0	$0	1	
C	C6	C	N	I	Y	$15	$15	Y	Y			$3,000	1	$3,000	80%	$10,000	$2,000	2	$4
D	PPO		N	I	Y	$15	$15	Y	Y			$1,000	3	$3,000	80%	$10,000	$2,000	3	$6
G	C		N	A	Y	$30	$30	Y	N			$750	2	$1,500	80%	$10,000	$2,000	2	$4
A	C		N	I	Y	$30	$30	Y	Y		$2,000	$1,000	3	$3,000	50%	$6,000	$3,000	3	$9
A	A		N	I	Y	$15	$15	Y	Y		$2,000	$2,500	3	$7,500	80%	$4,000	$800	3	$2
A	B		N	I	Y	$25	$25	Y	Y		$2,000	$5,000	3	$15,000	70%	$6,000	$1,800	3	$5
A	O	A	N	E	Y	$20	$20	Y	Y			$1,000	3	$3,000	80%	$10,000	$2,000	2	$4
K	K		N	A	Y	$0	$0	Y	N			$3,000	3	$9,000	70%	$13,333	$4,000	3	$12
A	C		N	I	Y	$30	$30	Y	Y		$2,000	$5,000	3	$15,000	50%	$6,000	$3,000	3	$9
M	M	M	N	E	Y	$25	$25	Y	Y			$1,500	3	$4,500	80%	$12,500	$2,500	2	$5
I	I		N	A	N	$100	$100	N	N			$25,000	1	$25,000	0%	$0	$0	1	
L	V		N	A	N	$25	$25	N	N			$3,000	3	$9,000	80%	$65,000	$13,000	3	$39
										MIN	$2,000	$250	1	$750	0%	$0	$0	1	
										MAX	$2,000	$25,000	3	$25,000	100%	$65,000	$13,000	5	$39

Figure 8.2: Example Spreadsheet Comparing Policies, Deductibles, Copays

with the follow-up sales call from an agent to answer questions and to try to make the sale. The fourth type doesn't give you any information until an agent calls, which can be good or bad: you don't start with certain expectations about the rate until you've talked through some of the features. However, the agent may not provide as many quotes so you won't get to know the entire breadth of coverage available.

Create Your Spreadsheet

Now we'll look at an example of a spreadsheet made for comparing this information, as shown in Figure 8.2. Each of the categories of the spreadsheet will be presented, followed by a detailed discussion of the major columns in the spreadsheet. If you are not familiar with spreadsheets, think of a worksheet that you fill out and the math is done for you.

Each of the sections of the spreadsheet contain information from each plan on one line. To create the spreadsheet, the financial numbers that you need for each plan are:

- Limits (Annual, Lifetime, Other – i.e. mental annual)
- Deductible – Dollar amount and number of family members
- Prescriptions – any coverage, deductible or maximum
- Copays – regular doctor, specialist
- Lab coverage
- Preventative care

										Label	Weight
									Composite	Best Case	2
fits	$50									Indiv Worst	1
penses	$500.00									Fam Worst	1
								Current Age			
								38			
								Years until 65 (Current Medicare Age)			
								27			
Premium		Out of Pocket (OOP)			Totals w/ Office Visit, Labs, Premiums			Best Case Until 65 (not inflation/increase adjusted)			

Monthly Premium	Annual Premium	Indiv. OOP	Family OOP	OV	OV+Lab	Best Case	Indiv Worst Case	Fam Worst Case	Best Case Until 65	Worst Case Individual Until 65	Worst Case Family Until 65	Composite Score
$334	$4,003	$7,725	$7,725	$825	$825	$4,828	$12,553	$12,553	$130,345	$338,920	$338,920	3
$327	$3,919	$5,500	$5,500	$2,000	$2,100	$6,019	$11,519	$11,519	$162,512	$311,012	$311,012	3
$317	$3,805	$10,000	$10,000	$825	$825	$4,630	$14,630	$14,630	$125,022	$395,022	$395,022	5
$351	$4,213	$6,500	$13,000	$600	$600	$4,813	$11,313	$17,813	$129,953	$305,453	$480,953	5
$205	$2,458	$10,500	$10,500	$2,000	$2,100	$4,558	$15,058	$15,058	$123,062	$406,562	$406,562	5
$446	$5,353	$5,450	$5,450	$2,000	$2,100	$7,453	$12,903	$12,903	$201,236	$348,386	$348,386	6
$579	$6,945	$5,000	$7,000	$300	$300	$7,245	$12,245	$14,245	$195,612	$330,612	$384,612	6
$591	$7,087	$3,000	$9,000	$300	$300	$7,387	$10,387	$16,387	$199,438	$280,438	$442,438	6
$708	$8,497	$2,750	$5,500	$600	$600	$9,097	$11,847	$14,597	$245,615	$319,865	$394,115	8
$564	$6,771	$4,000	$12,000	$600	$600	$7,371	$11,371	$19,371	$199,020	$307,020	$523,020	8
$675	$8,106	$3,300	$9,900	$300	$300	$8,406	$11,706	$18,306	$226,949	$316,049	$494,249	9
$524	$6,288	$6,800	$20,400	$500	$500	$6,788	$13,588	$27,188	$183,276	$366,876	$734,076	13
$910	$10,915	$3,000	$7,000	$400	$400	$11,315	$14,315	$18,315	$305,494	$386,494	$494,494	13
$568	$6,816	$7,000	$21,000	$0	$0	$6,816	$13,816	$27,816	$184,032	$373,032	$751,032	13
$477	$5,724	$8,000	$24,000	$600	$600	$6,324	$14,324	$30,324	$170,758	$386,758	$818,758	14
$967	$11,609	$4,500	$9,000	$500	$500	$12,109	$16,609	$21,109	$326,941	$448,441	$569,941	17
$149	$1,782	$25,000	$25,000	$2,000	$2,100	$3,882	$28,882	$28,882	$104,827	$779,827	$779,827	18
$481	$5,768	$16,000	$48,000	$500	$600	$6,368	$22,368	$54,368	$171,927	$603,927	$1,467,927	30
$149	$1,782	$250	$750	0	0	$3,548	$10,060	$11,519	$95,794	$271,629	$311,012	3 MIN
$1,123	$13,477	$25,000	$48,000	2000	2100	$13,777	$28,882	$54,368	$371,975	$779,827	$1,467,927	30 MAX

Figure 8.2 (continued): Example Spreadsheet Comparing Policies, Deductibles, Copays

The information for each of these categories will be detailed in the next few pages, along with the simple calculations that can be done with the numbers to help you determine your best deal. Sometimes it can be hard to find this information in the quotes provided. Your agent can help you to decipher them.

Remember that since some features are more important to you than others, you'll need to determine how much importance you want to give to each number. For example, my family is not currently on any prescription drugs, and we've only made use of the occasional antibiotic over the last few years. We didn't put much emphasis on the prescription side of the plan since our experience with generic antibiotics shows that they only cost a few dollars which was less than the prescription copay on our previous insurance!

Estimates

You need to make a few estimates about how you might use healthcare. You can use the information that you gathered in Chapter 5 to get an idea of how many of the types of items in Figure 8.3 that you use over the next year(s). This information is unique to you and your family, and it's just your best guess, since you can't know exactly what will happen – which is why you are insuring. These estimates can be used to calculate the overall cost to you for any policies or options that your are comparing, even those from the same insurer.

Annual Estimates	
1. Number of Wellness Office Visits	5
2. Number of Sick Office Visits	15
3. Well Visit Labs Cost	$100
4. Sick Visit Labs Cost	$0
5. Prescription Costs	$0
6. HSA Allowable Expenses	$500

Figure 8.3: Annual Estimates Section of Spreadsheet

1. Number of Wellness Office Visits

You are taking the count of well office visits from the work you completed in Chapter 5. The count is important since some plans have a copayment for each visit and some have the dollar amount for visits. If each of your family members will have an annual wellness visit, then put the number of family members. If you have a baby, then there may be an extra number of visits the first years, after which it will be annually. If you are not planning an annual wellness visit, you may wish to consider it, especially if your health plan offers to cover the visits. Sometimes a potentially serious condition is found during a wellness visit, and if caught early, can have a better outcome for your health.

2. Number of Sick Office Visits

You are taking the count of sick office visits from the work you completed in Chapter 5. Again, you'll want to be able to compare the count with the dollar amount. If you have kids or always get certain seasonal illnesses, then you'll want to be sure to include the number of sick visits that your family typically makes.

3. Well Visit Labs Cost

If you make well visits, then you can get an idea of how much the lab costs are from Chapter 5, or specifically from an explanation of benefits from your well visits. If you were using a network and plan to continue using a network, then use the discounted numbers, otherwise use the full price numbers. If you haven't been getting wellness care but think that you might, you can contact your provider and ask about how much the lab work would cost, both from a list price and a typical provider amount. You can ask how much a certain insurer pays if the provider is cooperative.

4. Sick Visit Labs Cost

Look at the costs for the lab work in Chapter 5. If you were using a network and plan to continue using a network, then use the discounted numbers, otherwise use the full price numbers. It's hard to know about how much unpredictable sick lab costs will be, but you can predict the typical things like strep tests for children. Again, refer to explanation of benefits statements or call your provider for this information.

5. Prescription Costs

If you have had prescriptions, then you'll be able to look at the paperwork from the prescriptions to find out how much the full price is and how much insurance covers, as you may have done in Chapter 5.

> ⚡ When trying to figure out my prescription costs, I contacted a pharmacy and found that they were very helpful in giving medication prices. I was surprised to find that they offer a 10% discount off list price for those without a prescription plan.

6. HSA Allowable Expenses

If you are in a high enough tax bracket, there is a benefit to using the HSA savings account to pay medical expenses such that they are "tax free" when using the HSA dollars. If your income is low enough, less than approximately $50,000 a year for a family of four, there may not be any tax advantages to using these dollars. If your income is really high, then you might want to use the HSA account for long term savings and pay for expenses with your regular dollars, in order to build the HSA account balance for long term needs.

You may have more eligible expenses than the insurance would cover, or simply the deductible and coinsurance. In either case, you can make a total amount here and use this information to determine how you can reduce your overall cost of insurance by using "tax free" dollars, if you are in a tax bracket high enough to see savings. For most people the HSA Allowable amount will be the same as the total amount from Chapter 5, unless you are going to be able to use your HSA dollars to pay for things that your plan will not cover, such as alternative medical treatments like massage and acupuncture.

Totaling Up Your Estimates

The point of making the estimates is to allow you to come up with a total estimated amount that you would spend on a year with health insurance. You'll use the total from Chapter 5 along with the numbers above to calculate how much things would cost without insurance, with copayment type plans, and with deductible plans. One very important thing to remember is that no matter how much comparison you do, you're always comparing apples to oranges – since one plan may pay for things that another will not, and some copayments cover everything that happens at the doctor's office, such as labs and treatments, and others don't. So this is approximate, but close enough to allow you to compare between plans.

Total Wellness Visit Estimate = Number of Wellness Office Visits x Your Office Visit Cost.

Total Sick Visit Estimate = Number of Sick Office Visits x Your Office Visit Cost.

Basic Information About a Policy

This section starts the gathering of information about each potential health insurance policy, shown in Figure 8.4. In many cases you may be comparing the same product from the same company but with a difference in deductible, co-insurance, or copayment. It is worth comparing different versions of the same policy since your needs and your financial situation are unique, and you may find that one configuration from a particular insurer is very attractive, but others are not so attractive. You can also see the interrelation between the deductible and coinsurance at work, which will really help you to "get it" and make the decision about whether you want higher premiums paid to the insurer, or whether you would like to take a lower premium and save/invest the difference yourself.

Company	Plan	Network	HSA/ HDHP	Type: I=Individual A=Association E=Employee
A	H	A	Y	I
G	HSA		Y	A
A	H	A	Y	I
G	O	GC	N	A
I	HSA		Y	A
J	HSA		Y	A
C	C6	C	N	I
D	PPO		N	I
G	C		N	A
A	C		N	I
A	A		N	I
A	B		N	I
A	O	A	N	E
K	K		N	A
A	C		N	I
M	M	M	N	E
I	I		N	A
L	V		N	A

Figure 8.4: Basic Information Section of Spreadsheet

Company

Make a note of the company name (abbreviations are OK). You'll want to remember which is which once you've gone through the trouble of gathering all the information.

Plan

The plan name from the company will help you to remember which is which.

Network

If a network is part of the plan, you may have a choice between networks. For example, one plan that I reviewed had a choice of two networks, one larger than the other. I reviewed the two networks and decided that the smaller network met my needs and found that there was a price savings using the smaller network.

HSA/HDHP

Some plans are qualified to be part of an HSA/HDHP combination. You may want to consider an HSA/HDHP for any potential tax savings, so make sure you note which plans are HSA eligible here.

Type: Individual, Association, or Employer

As covered in Chapter 6, association plans are different than individual and employer group plans. Make a note as to the type of the plan and also the source (employer, spouse, etc. from Chapter 3). If you end up needing to work with more than one agent, you can also note that here for your convenience.

Deductible

Comparing deductibles from plans within the same company can be as beneficial as comparing deductibles from other companies. One thought is how "comfortable" you feel with a certain deductible. Another is whether you have the financial means to pay the deductible amount, whether from an emergency fund, family, or financing, including using a credit card, though this should be your last choice. The hardest number to find on some plans is the number of family members that will have to meet the deductible before the plan pays for everything. The deductibles section of the spreadsheet is shown in Figure 8.5.

Individual	Family Max #	Family
$5,450	1	$5,450
$5,500	1	$5,500
$10,000	1	$10,000
$2,500	2	$5,000
$10,500	1	$10,500
$5,450	1	$5,450
$3,000	1	$3,000
$1,000	3	$3,000
$750	2	$1,500
$1,000	3	$3,000
$2,500	3	$7,500
$5,000	3	$15,000
$1,000	3	$3,000
$3,000	3	$9,000
$5,000	3	$15,000
$1,500	3	$4,500
$25,000	1	$25,000
$3,000	3	$9,000

Figure 8.5: Deductible Section of Spreadsheet

Individual Deductible Dollar Amount

This is usually quoted right up front, and can appear in the name of the plan.

Number of Family Members to Meet Family Deductible

This number can be a little tricky to find, since it isn't the most prominent number. The difference in number of family members between plans can be significant.

Total Family Deductible

In most cases, the total deductible for a family is simply the number of family members times the individual deductible.

Coinsurance

Gather the coinsurance information here, as it is important to computing your total out-of-pocket. The spreadsheet section is shown in Figure 8.6.

Percentage

The percentage numbers tend to be confusing. The larger number is what the insurance company pays, the smaller number is what you pay. Some quote it one way, some another, so one quote that says 20% coinsurance is really the same as another company's 80% coinsurance. 100%, 90%, 80%, 70%, and 50% are popular percentages.

Limit in Dollar Amount

It may take a minute to figure out how the company is portraying the limit on the dollar amount. Some companies will say that you pay 20% of the next $10,000, and some will say that coinsurance is 80% up to $2,000. This is just two ways of saying the same thing.

%	Limit	Individual Max	Family Max #	Family Max
50%	$4,550	$2,275	1	$2,275
100%	$0	$0	1	$0
100%	$0	$0	1	$0
50%	$8,000	$4,000	2	$8,000
0%	$0	$0	1	$0
0%	$0	$0	1	$0
80%	$10,000	$2,000	2	$4,000
80%	$10,000	$2,000	3	$6,000
80%	$10,000	$2,000	2	$4,000
50%	$6,000	$3,000	3	$9,000
80%	$4,000	$800	3	$2,400
70%	$6,000	$1,800	3	$5,400
80%	$10,000	$2,000	2	$4,000
70%	$13,333	$4,000	3	$12,000
50%	$6,000	$3,000	3	$9,000
80%	$12,500	$2,500	2	$5,000
0%	$0	$0	1	$0
80%	$65,000	$13,000	3	$39,000

Figure 8.6: Coinsurance Section of Spreadsheet

Individual Maximum Dollar Amount

This is the coinsurance percent that you would pay (the smaller percent) times the maximum amount of coinsurance. Sometimes it is directly provided by the insurer, but you should make sure you have the right number.

Number of Family Members

There are a number of family members that must satisfy the coinsurance before the insurance company pays for everything. It is usually the same number as the number that must satisfy the deductible.

Total Family Coinsurance Dollar Amount

This is the Individual Maximum Dollar Amount times the Number of Family Members.

Premium

The premium is how much you pay for the insurance itself. Payment of premiums is typically monthly, with many companies using an automatic payment plan from your checking account. Since the analysis, and the benefit period, tend to be for a year, you'll multiply the monthly premium quoted by twelve to get an annual premium. The premium section is shown in Figure 8.7.

Monthly Premium

The quoted amount for the coverage. Some plans may also have an association fee (an association) or a account maintenance fee (a small group policy for your business). Be sure to add these in as it helps to know your total monthly cost.

Annual Premium

The Monthly Premium times twelve. This amount can change during the year depending on the terms of your policy and the laws of the state in which the policy is written. This can be your state if it is an individual policy written to you, a group policy written to your company, or a different state if it is an out-of-state association. The likely times that the premium might change are after a birthday (typically ages ending in zero and five), after adding additional dependents, and usually at the renewal period or the calendar year, depending on which calendar the insurer uses. Your agent will have an idea of which insurer increases premiums when, how frequently, and how much.

Monthly Premium	Annual Premium
$334	$4,003
$327	$3,919
$317	$3,805
$351	$4,213
$205	$2,458
$446	$5,353
$579	$6,945
$591	$7,087
$708	$8,497
$564	$6,771
$675	$8,106
$524	$6,288
$910	$10,915
$568	$6,816
$477	$5,724
$967	$11,609
$149	$1,782
$481	$5,768

Figure 8.7: Premium Section of Spreadsheet

Out of Pocket Maximum

The out of pocket maximum expense is how much you stand to loose if things go wrong, shown in Figure 8.8. Your exposure without any health insurance is unlimited to the maximum amount of healthcare you could possibly consume. I'm using it as an annual amount that you stand to loose if things go horribly wrong medically. There are additional expenses that you might incur that would not be covered by any health insurance. Things like transportation, child care, lost wages, and more that would be above and beyond the exposure amount. The exposure can show how much money you could be "out" if you have a medical problem during a year on a health insurance plan.

Individual OOP	Family OOP
$7,725	$7,725
$5,500	$5,500
$10,000	$10,000
$6,500	$13,000
$10,500	$10,500
$5,450	$5,450
$5,000	$7,000
$3,000	$9,000
$2,750	$5,500
$4,000	$12,000
$3,300	$9,900
$6,800	$20,400
$3,000	$7,000
$7,000	$21,000
$8,000	$24,000
$4,500	$9,000
$25,000	$25,000
$16,000	$48,000

Individual Out of Pocket (OOP) Maximum

This is the amount that you would be responsible for one individual who may have a medical event. Other expenses for other family members would still need to meet the out of pocket maximum until you reach the Family Out of Pocket Maximum.

Figure 8.8: Out of Pocket Maximum Section of Spreadsheet

Family Out of Pocket (OOP) Maximum

The Family Out of Pocket Maximum is calculated by multiplying the Individual Out of Pocket Maximum by the maximum number of family members for the deductible/coinsurance.

Options

Each plan under consideration has options. Some are part of the plan that you choose, others are add-ons. From a financial comparison perspective, some of the more important ones are the inclusion of laboratory work and copay amount. See the example shown in Figure 8.9.

Labs Included?

Sometimes labs will be included, sometimes they are included to a certain limit. See if this is a factor for you and note whether these are covered for each plan. My wife thought that the labs would be a big factor, especially for annual wellness visits. It turns out that the explanation of benefits shows that the lab fees of over $200 are discounted to the insurance company to the $20 range, if you see an "in-network" laboratory. Overall we found that our expected lab work outside of a major medical event wasn't significant enough to use this as a strong factor in our choice. Knowing that for hospitalization labs would be included was a big relief for any major medical events.

Labs Included?	Office Visit Copay
N	$55
N	$100
N	$55
Y	$30
N	$100
N	$100
Y	$15
Y	$15
Y	$30
Y	$30
Y	$15
Y	$25
Y	$20
Y	$0
Y	$30
Y	$25
N	$100
N	$25

Figure 8.9: Options Section of Spreadsheet

Office Visit Copay

Office visit copays can range from $10 to $40 (or more). If a plan offers this option, note the amount here. I was surprised to learn from the explanation of benefits that our average doctor visit, after the network discount, was only about $55. Remember also that you can get more value than just the doctor's fees when using a copayment. Some cover everything that happens in the doctor's office, not just the doctors time: things like lab tests and immunizations done during the same visit. Indemnity insurance will not have a copay – and the deductible will apply to all eligible expenses at full list price, and not a network discount price.

Wellness

Some plans include wellness separately from office visits. For HSA/HDHP plans, this can be included while copayments for other office visits are specifically not allowed. This is shown in Figure 8.10.

Wellness Visit Copay

Note this number: you'll multiply it by the number of wellness visits to come up with a cost for this plan for wellness. If wellness is included and there is no copay, then use zero for this number, and the additional cost for wellness is zero (it's included in the premiums).

Wellness Labs Included?

Some labs may be included for wellness. Use this factor to decide whether wellness labs will be included in the premium, or cost extra.

Prescriptions

If you really need a plan to pay for prescriptions, then you may have a condition that would up-rate you, and the comparison that you will do between plans may not be done without some idea of what the higher rates would be from particular insurers for your condition, so talk to your agent about this. However, you can use the readily available quoted rates to find out the better combination of deductible/coinsurance for you. A prescriptions spreadsheet section is shown in Figure 8.11.

Included Y/N?

Some plans have prescriptions, others don't. If this is important to you, then track it. Keep in mind that generic drugs, such as typical penicillin formulations and pain relievers can be extremely inexpensive. The amount that you spend on prescriptions may be less than the amount that you pay for a prescription benefit if you use prescriptions infrequently.

Prescription Deductible

Some plans have a deductible that you must meet before you are eligible for benefits related to prescriptions.

Maximum

Opposite to the deductible, on some plans prescriptions have an upper limit of benefit.

Well Office Visit Copay	Well Labs Y/N
$0	Y
$100	N
$0	Y
$30	Y
$100	N
$100	N
$15	Y
$15	Y
$30	Y
$30	Y
$15	Y
$25	Y
$20	Y
$0	Y
$30	Y
$25	Y
$100	N
$25	N

Figure 8.10: Wellness Section of Spreadsheet

Prescription Y/N	Prescription Deductible	Prescription Maximum
Y	$0	$2,000
N	$0	
Y	$0	$2,000
N	$0	
N	$0	
N	$0	
Y	$0	
Y	$0	
N	$0	
Y	$0	$2,000
Y	$0	$2,000
Y	$0	$2,000
Y	$0	
N	$0	
Y	$0	$2,000
Y	$0	
N	$0	
N	$0	

Figure 8.11: Prescriptions Section of Spreadsheet

Totals

These totals are interesting to review since they are an excellent basis for comparing the financial costs of health insurance and use during a year. The spreadsheet totals are shown in Figure 8.12.

Best Case = Office Visits + Labs + Annual Premium + Prescription Costs

The best case you could experience with a prospective plan is to take the total amount that you would spend on your anticipated yearly expenses, and then add the annual cost of the plan. Of course, the number might be lower for one plan than another, which is why this number is useful for comparing multiple plans with each other.

To figure this number out, multiply the number of well office visits by the well office copay or doctors fee. Then add the number of sicks visits times the standard copay or doctors fee. Include the cost of labs if they are not included in your policy, the annual premium, and the costs of prescriptions that you might have on the given plan.

Best Case	Individual Worst Case	Family Worst Case
$4,828	$12,553	$12,553
$6,019	$11,519	$11,519
$4,630	$14,630	$14,630
$4,813	$11,313	$17,813
$4,558	$15,058	$15,058
$7,453	$12,903	$12,903
$7,245	$12,245	$14,245
$7,387	$10,387	$16,387
$9,097	$11,847	$14,597
$7,371	$11,371	$19,371
$8,406	$11,706	$18,306
$6,788	$13,588	$27,188
$11,315	$14,315	$18,315
$6,816	$13,816	$27,816
$6,324	$14,324	$30,324
$12,109	$16,609	$21,109
$3,882	$28,882	$28,882
$6,368	$22,368	$54,368

Figure 8.12: Totals Section of Spreadsheet

Individual Worst Case = Best Case + Individual Out of Pocket

If one family member has a medical event and covered expenses exceed the deductible and coinsurance, then you'll end up paying this amount and the insurer will pay the rest. Of course, the total could be higher if another family member has a less serious medical event, or expenses that are not covered are incurred. That's why the family worst case is also important to consider if you are insuring more than one person.

Family Worst Case = Best Case + Family Out of Pocket Maximum

In the unlikely event that more than one family member has a serious medical event, the maximum that you would pay in a year for premiums, doctor's visits, and covered expenses for the medical events is this number. This is also useful for comparison between plans to determine how much you might be responsible for financially in this situation.

Best/Worst Case Until Medicare

Currently the requirements for Medicare eligibility are working at least 10 years in eligible employment, and having social security or railroad retirement benefits (among other special cases). Calculating how much you might pay for a certain plan (in current dollars) until you reach this milestone can amplify some of the differences that you see in plans. My time frame at this writing is at least 27 years until Medicare eligibility, so my numbers reflect this. Your numbers will be greater or lesser depending on your age and the age of family members. More complex formulas could be devised for other family sizes and ages – and mine doesn't include eventually having to drop the children from the policy as they are no longer eligible dependents, nor does it include age related increases (but perhaps these two factors would cancel each other out.). The best/worst case spreadsheet section is shown in Figure 8.13

Best Case Until 65	Worst Case Individual Until 65	Worst Case Family Until 65
$130,345	$338,920	$338,920
$162,512	$311,012	$311,012
$125,022	$395,022	$395,022
$129,953	$305,453	$480,953
$123,062	$406,562	$406,562
$201,236	$348,386	$348,386
$195,612	$330,612	$384,612
$199,438	$280,438	$442,438
$245,615	$319,865	$394,115
$199,020	$307,020	$523,020
$226,949	$316,049	$494,249
$183,276	$366,876	$734,076
$305,494	$386,494	$494,494
$184,032	$373,032	$751,032
$170,758	$386,758	$818,758
$326,941	$448,441	$569,941
$104,827	$779,827	$779,827
$171,927	$603,927	$1,467,927

Figure 8.13: Best/Worst Case Until Medicare Section of Spreadsheet

Best Case Until 65

The best case times the number of years until you are eligible. In my research for my family, I found that this number ranged from $95,000 to $741,000. I favored the lower end of this range, since this meant that my annual minimum expense for health insurance and healthcare would be reasonably low.

Worst Case Individual Until 65

The individual worst case times the number of years until you are eligible. In my research for my family, I found that this number ranged from $271,000 to $1,011,000. Again, I favored the lower end of this range because the reason that health insurance is so important to me is to cover the big money if something goes really wrong, like a family member with a serious condition year after year, hitting the individual maximum.

Worst Case Family Until 65

The family worst case times the number of years until you are eligible. This ranged from $311,000 to $1,467,927 which is really a lot of money! Again, I favored the lower end of this range because with this much money involved, I want to keep costs down as much as possible. This scenario would mean that more than one family member, up to the total number of family members in the deductible/coinsurance, had serious conditions requiring medical care in excess of the total out of pocket each year.

Composite Score

I created a composite score in my calculations because I had so much information from so many companies, shown in Figure 8.14. I used a formula that gave the best case and the individual worst case equal weight, so that I could minimize both of these but keep them about the same in importance. I then picked the top 10 and reviewed the details of these to make my choice.

Composite Score
3
3
5
5
5
6
6
6
8
8
9
13
13
13
14
17
18
30

Figure 8.14: Composite Score Section of Spreadsheet

A Formula to Create a Composite Score

((Best Case – Lowest Best Case) x Best Case Weight Factor
+ (Individual Worst Case – Lowest Individual Worst Case) x Individual Worst Case Weight Factor
+ (Family Worst Case – Lowest Family Worst Case) x Family Worst Case Weight)
/ (A Normalization Factor That Makes The Numbers Easier To Compare)

An Example:

(($4,630 – $3,548) x 2 + ($14,630 – $10,060) x 1 + ($14,630 – $11,519) x 1) / 2000

The composite score was created by adding the best case factor, the individual worst case factor, and the family worst case factor, then multiplying that by a weight factor. I used 2 for the best case weight since I felt that the overall cost was twice as important as the worst case for an individual, and family, for both of which I used a weight of 1. You'll need to determine which numbers work best for your situation.

Summary

Here are some interesting things that I hope you learn from doing the calculations in this chapter.

Different policies and/or terms from the same company provide different value for you. Some save you money in premiums, some cut down your out of pocket worst case risk. Some offerings are at the best value and at the worst value from the same company. The best care is not necessarily the most expensive. The reputation of the company, type of policy, and how well it meets your needs are far better ways to pick the plan than price alone. You can get reasonably priced policies from the best companies.

> 💡 Your best deal may not be to write a large check every month to a health insurer in exchange for ten dollar doctor's visits and a $250 deductible at the hospital. If you were to save and invest the difference between the annual premium for this type of plan, and the premium for a high deductible plan, you could save the difference in deductible in about 18 months and keep saving.

Different companies may have policies in all price ranges and in all value ranges (a measure of how good of a deal it is for you). You can choose the top 10 (or 20) of your research and narrow it down based on all other criteria. For example, the top plan in my calculations, one that I didn't choose, offered a slightly higher long-term payment ($12,000 over the next 27 years) than the one I chose, but had a worst case maximum of $50,000 less than the one I chose. I figure that I can save/invest the $12,000 myself and if I continue to focus on wellness (which is good for so many more reasons than just not making health insurance claims), that the chance of not needing to spend the additional $2,000 a year in benefits (50,000 – 12,000 = 38,000) will work to my advantage.

I hope that even if you're not a numbers person, that you can still take these valuable observations, and manage to get the numbers together with help from others. Downloads, online tools (including picture graphs) for this chapter can be found at www.BestHealthInsuranceBook.com.

Chapter 9

Make Your Choice

It's time to choose. You've learned the terms, estimated your annual expenditures, found licensed insurers and agents, compared features and quotes, and thought about every conceivable place to get coverage. But what health insurance have you got now? This is an important factor in choosing which type of insurance you may go to. This is particularly important if you or a family member has a medical condition.

Take Into Consideration What You've Got Now

Either you've got insurance or you don't, and if you've got insurance, then it comes from one of a few places. Taking into account what you've got now helps you to choose options for what you should get next. Figure 9.1 discusses some of the typical options for people based on what they've got now. Of course, there are more options, and more creative options than these. For starters, you can mix and match these approaches for different family members and put individuals on their own policy.

If You've Got Health Insurance From An Employer...

Option 1: If you are staying at your employer, consider better rates or owning an individual policy.

Option 2: If you are leaving, consider an individual policy if you are healthy, COBRA if you have a medical condition, either if you are somewhere in the middle. Once COBRA runs out for those with a medical condition, a HIPAA conversion policy will keep coverage, at a price, but it may be cheaper than paying medical bills without insurance.

If You've Got an Individual Policy...

Option 1: If you want to keep an individual policy, you're not subject to losing coverage when changing employment. If you are in the healthiest tier then you keep the best rate for life. You're not subject to COBRA or HIPAA if you lose your job and you have a medical condition. If you're healthy, consider reviewing your deductible, coinsurance, copayments, and an HSA/HDHP. If you've got a medical condition, talk to your current insurer about options available without medical underwriting. Your insurer may have limits about how often and when you can change plans with them, and may also have changes that you can make that do not require medical underwriting.

Option 2: If you are moving to an employer policy, especially one that is employer subsidized, you may get a better rate for those with medical conditions who don't have a good individual rate, but you'll be unlikely to come back and get a good individual rate if you leave an individual policy. However, if you have a medical condition and leave that employer policy, then you may face difficulties getting insurance or getting a reasonable rate.

If You've Got Association Group Sold to Individuals...

Option 1: If you want to move to an individual policy, you won't be subject to getting stuck in an unhealthy group. If it's an out of state association then go in-state for the benefit of having one department of insurance to resolve issues.

Option 2: If you want to move to employer plan, then it's the same as from an individual policy option 2 above.

If You've Got Your Own Company Plan...

Option 1: If you want to keep the company plan, the rates depend on the experience of your group. Poorer health will drive rates up, but not as much as individual because they are usually capped more stringently by the state. You may not be able to get individual insurance, or get it affordably, if you have a medical condition. You can change insurers regularly and get guaranteed issue.

Option 2: If you want to move to an individual policy, if you're healthy, then rates can be better and current tax laws can help with deductions for these expenses.

If You've Got Nothing...

Option 1: Start with something – individual, your company group, employer group, association group – in that order for those fortunate to be healthy. If you have a significant medical condition, then an employer group (the larger the employer, usually the better) or your own company group.

Figure 9.1: Consider What You've Got Now

If you are on an employer group plan, and have a sick family member, then staying with that employer plan is a good choice. If you are unable to do that, then you will probably want to consider the COBRA option – available from employers with more than 20 employees – which means that you will pay the employer cost, plus a few percent, for probably 18 months. You may find this to be expensive compared to what you were paying as an employee. At the end of this time, you are eligible to take a HIPAA guaranteed policy, but this will not be cheap either. In fact, it may cost more than the COBRA amount. But consider how much your medical bills would be without insurance, and compare to insurance costs that might be $1,500/month x 12 months = $18,000/year. Compare that to the medical cost of the condition and you'll figure out the best choice, keeping in mind any additional conditions that may occur because of the current condition, conditions for other family members, and the risks of not having insurance. Of course, if another job with health benefits is possible, or your spouse getting employment, then that's good too. Just remember that there may be a waiting period for any pre-existing condition. If you've had an ongoing business, perhaps part-time on the side, and it generates enough money to more than pay for health insurance, then a small business group plan may work: consider insuring each spouse separately as an employee, with the healthier one taking on any eligible dependents, and look into individual policies for dependents.

> ☞ Changing or re-applying at the same company may have limits on how frequently you can change and/or re-apply, typically once a year.

Choose Your Best Deal

It's finally time to make your choice. You've gone through the features, gotten a list of licensed insurers, narrowed the list, gotten quotes from those companies, and figured out your best case and worst case financial numbers. Now it comes down to reviewing the costs and making sure that you are comfortable

Review Costs

Chapter 8 dealt with all sorts of financial numbers including figuring out your bottom line. Make sure that you understand your monthly and annual costs for the health insurance, along with what is and

> ☞ "Insurance is to protect what you cannot self insure. An example is your house versus a light bulb. If the light bulb burns out, you can replace that yourself. If your house burns down you can't replace that by yourself without going into some kind of financial catastrophe. That's when you want insurance."
> *-Lauren Gadkowski Lindsay, CFP®, NAPFA Registered Financial Advisor, Personal Financial Advisors*

is not covered. You'll have a certain amount of out-of-pocket expense each year in almost every case, so make sure you understand what that is, and look at how many months you'll have to save to cover that out-of-pocket expense. You have the choice of paying more to the insurance company and having them manage your deductible, but you may find that you can do a better job of it if you focus on wellness and save and invest the money that represents the difference between premiums. I figured that within 16 months I would have saved the difference between a high-deductible ($10,000 for my family) and a low deductible plan. The only thing left to remember is that you could be responsible for that amount year after year for medical care that is covered, and still have to pay for anything that is not covered in your policy, too. Which leads to the next section, your comfort.

Determine How You are Most Comfortable

What good is insurance if you are not comfortable with the terms of it? Now, comfort is a relative thing. Without a broad view of available options, I doubt that I would be comfortable with a high deductible plan, much less a deductible of any amount. But the financial perspective brought by Chapter 8 really helps to see how the numbers stack up, and how much each of the configurations will cost. Plus, my choice is certainly not the right one for everyone else, and your choice must fit for you. I must admit that I've had a little practice getting used to the idea of a high deductible. Following financial advice, I raised the deductible on my house and automobiles to lower the premium and haven't had an issue with that decision since.

During the process of researching and writing this book, I had to go back many times to the choice that I had made. I originally made a choice and bought a plan that I thought would work well for me. But I worried at night while going to bed about little things here and there that I had learned. In the end I went back to the health insurance agent and changed my insurer to the one suggested in the first place, but not in the initial configuration. The spreadsheet had opened my eyes to the various financial options, and I had spotted a few that would work for me on a financial and emotional level. I recall being asked how much of a deductible I would be comfortable with, and not knowing enough, the deductibles that were under consideration were much lower than I am actually comfortable with. You must determine which insurer and set of numbers you are comfortable with. If there is more than one acceptable choice, put it in priority order, sleep on it, and then make the best of those choices. If you need a little help making the final choice, choose quality of company over cost since you are buying quality and quality may cost a little more. Then it's back to the agent to make the application.

> ☼ The impact of unexpected health care costs can destroy your financial life. That is why risk management is part of a comprehensive financial plan and strong catastrophic health insurance coverage is a key component of that plan. An individual or family can budget to cover deductibles and coinsurance in their routine expenses. It is much harder to meet large catastrophic health care costs—especially when they could be compounded by loss of income during recovery, etc. That makes catastrophic major medical coverage the primary goal in the selection of health insurance. Don't lose site of this goal in your search for coverage. If you do, the results could be devastating!
> -Margery K. Schiller, CFP®, NAPFA Registered Financial Advisor, Goar, Endriss & Walker, P.A.

Apply for Insurance

The health insurance application process can be tiresome and stressful: not knowing what you should or should not include when the form asks specific questions. Must you disclose false positives and diagnostic tests that ended up showing that you didn't have a condition? What about that one-time injury? Once you've determined your best plan, working with an agent to fill out the paperwork can reduce stress and ensure that you are given a fair shot at medical underwriting. What if you've forgotten about something?

> "A lot of people don't understand that if you go direct to an insurer, or you try to do it online, if you answer one question wrong it could affect you for a long time."
> -Jennifer McLaurin, Director of Sales, John F. Sipp & Associates

Chances are that if you've forgotten, it was probably minor, but you can check with your agent to determine if the information needs to be supplied.

Leaving out information intentionally can be construed as fraud in some cases. The insurer has the option to cancel your policy and return premiums minus any claims made. There may be time limitations on this that can vary by state, and also both federal and state laws that could send you to criminal court. Accidentally leaving something out might lead to denial of the claim at a minimum, and questions about whether you left it out intentionally.

Fill Out the Application

In order to make it as pleasant as possible, you should plan a couple of hours for this effort. First, gather your medical records and have them nearby should you have any questions or need help recalling anything.

> Health insurance doesn't start in a day or two, except short term. It takes several weeks to a month to get health insurance, so plan ahead if you can.

Then schedule time to fill out the application with your spouse if you're applying with him/her. Applications vary from insurer to insurer and state to state, but you're probably facing four, six, or more pages of small print questions. While going through the application, have a blank sheet of paper at hand to write down questions or concerns about the application so that you can go back to your agent (or the insurer) to resolve those questions.

Some applications are done online, even when working with an agent. It is in your best interest when filling one of these out to have an agent review it before submitting, since the agent will be aware of some of the underwriting idiosyncrasies of the company and can help avoid mistakes that can cost you. If you choose to go without an agent's review, you're taking the risk that something that you fill out may raise a flag due to a misunderstanding of the question being asked, and that can cost you money and possibly a denial of insurance, not to mention the entry of any negative information at the Medical Information Bureau – a "credit reporting" agency used by health and life insurers.

Once you've got your application completed, or nearly completed, you'll want to have it reviewed by your agent to spot any mistakes or to answer any questions. Along with the application you'll be expected to pay any application fee and also the first month's premium. Make sure that you make the premium payable to the insurance company and not the agent. This is standard practice and avoids any problems processing the funds and ensures that the money goes to the right place. Of course, in the rare occasion that any fees are due to the agent, they should be paid to the agent.

Paramedical Exam

Sometimes as part of the underwriting process, a medical examination is ordered. Once I had one for life insurance, but until recently never for purchasing medical insurance. The insurance company trusts that you have filled in your application properly, but sometimes they need to verify: either randomly or for specific reasons. Somehow I came up lucky this time, and had to be tested. But neither my wife or my kids had to be tested. Here's how it went:

> The insurance company may require more than a paramedical. It varies based on the information on your application. Sometimes they'll want doctors records. They could even require a comprehensive physical examination.

First, you put in your application for health insurance. Then a few days later someone calls from a separate company that does medical examinations for life and/or health insurance. You make an appointment within the next few days to a week, and the nurse comes to your home or place of business. The visit is short, and the first thing you give is an ID, such as a drivers license to make sure it's really you, and not some healthy body double. I was given a cup for a urine sample to provide during the time that the nurse was filling in the paperwork. Some examinations might be simple in nature, such as mine, that included height, weight, blood pressure, pulse, a few basic questions, and the urine sample. Some may be more complex, involving a blood draw, other body measurements, and more questions. You sign the consent for testing, allowing them to test for anything listed on the form. The things that they might test your blood or urine for include HIV/AIDS, heart disease, coronary artery disease, liver disorders, kidney disorders, diabetes, viral hepatitis, prostate disease, immune disorders, nicotine, medications, cocaine, other frequently abused drugs, or anything else that the insurer deems necessary.

The paperwork and any samples are then usually sent by courier to a laboratory that specializes in this type of testing. They generally run the tests as soon as possible after receiving them. Their results are very quick, and sent over to the insurer rapidly. Assuming that there are no bumps in the road, or other pending information, they'll complete their underwriting of your application, and make a decision to insure or not, whether any exclusionary riders are necessary, and what rate to give to you.

By the way, if anything bad shows up during these tests, it will be reported to the Medical Information Bureau (MIB). However, if there are any false positives, and you are able to correct the information through additional medical testing, then the Medical Information Bureau information can also be corrected.

How do you get ready for the medical exam? First of all, make sure that you are living your healthiest lifestyle. While it is never a good time to begin an unhealthy habit, it is always a good time to give one up. During the days, weeks, or months leading up to your health insurance application, you should be on your best healthy behavior. Drink plenty of water, rest well, and don't have anything too sugary or go on an eating binge prior to your medical examination because it may produce negative test results that may not typify your health.

Cancel Existing Insurance

Wait! Don't cancel yet. You still need to do a few things, just to make sure that what you ordered is what you got. Since everything that you've received so far refers to "the policy", you need to make sure that you have that in hand. You won't have a policy to review if you have employer group insurance or an association group. What you'll have instead is a certificate of coverage (refer to Chapter 6 for a discussion of the benefits and drawbacks to the different types). For either a policy or a certificate, the steps that you need to follow now are to receive the acceptance from the insurer, review the policy (or certificate), get any questions answered, make sure that the payment is valid, and then you can cancel any existing insurance.

Receive Acceptance

Different insurers call it different things, but basically they're offering you coverage at a price that they have determined through underwriting. If the price is not what was quoted, you should understand why the actual price that you are offered is higher or less frequently lower. You'll want to make sure that the offered policy premium is still a good deal by performing the calculations in Chapter 8. If you find that it is no longer a top contender, then you may wish to explore health insurance from a different insurer since they all underwrite differently and will calculate the insurance premiums differently. Sometimes you can appeal the rate with the insurer, which can take time and effort on your part.

Review Plan and Materials

I know that it isn't exciting, but you'll also want to read through the thick package of materials that come as part of the policy or certificate. You'll want to make sure that you understand what is covered and how, since most of the marketing materials refer to the policy/certificate for the final word on what is covered and how. In particular, look at the sections that are the most important to you, whether that be hospitalization, specific illnesses, or any of the myriad of features discussed in Chapter 4. If it isn't in the policy/certificate, then it's not covered, period. If you cannot find something that you thought should be in the policy, call the insurer or your agent. Make sure to document when you called and to whom you spoke, but remember ultimately it has to be in the written policy for it to be covered.

Get Answers to Any Questions

You may have questions when reading through the policy/certificate. Write these down as you're reading the document, referring to page, section, and paragraph so that when you get answers to the questions from your agent you'll both be able to efficiently find and answer the questions. If your agent is unavailable or hard to reach during your review period, you may also wish to contact the insurer or your state agency for insurance, especially if they have a consumer help hotline for people who are buying insurance. If you can't answer the questions and the answer is serious enough, then you may have to consider a different insurer or plan. It's better to find out now any problems that you might face, instead of after a big medical event that could potentially bankrupt you.

Ensure Payment

Make sure that not only your initial payment was good to the insurer, but that any payment plan that will pay the premiums on a monthly, quarterly, or other basis has correct account numbers and information. Having the insurer automatically take the payment from your bank account reduces the chance that a problem will occur in either the timing or scheduling of the payment. Having an additional linked savings account to a checking account will also ensure that if the checking account runs low that money will be available to make any payments from a savings account. You certainly don't want the insurance to be cancelled unintentionally when you're in the middle of a medical event and need the coverage most.

The insurance company payment is much less forgiving than a credit card might be. You may have a short period of time after the payment is due before your policy is cancelled, but if you miss this period, that's it. Your policy is cancelled due to lack of payment. If you are making claims, they will be rejected and you'll owe the full amount of those claims. So put your health insurance premiums toward the top of the list of bills to be paid, otherwise you'll have to re-apply, at a potentially higher rate, plus pay any bills that were rejected.

What About the Overlapping Month's Payment?

You don't really want to be paying double for your first month's insurance premium by paying for the new policy and the old one at the same time. This pitfall can occur if you don't have enough time between when you apply and when the payment is made on the old plan. Each insurer can tell you at the time of your application about how long to expect the underwriting to take. If you have fewer medical items in the application, and it matches any information at the MIB, then your application will go through very quickly. If there are many medical items to research, then it may take longer. You can ask for a different effective date if the insurance arrives without enough time to go through the above steps without paying for two insurers in the same month.

What About Skipping a Month of Payments?

You could conceivably skip a month of payments while moving from existing insurance to new insurance, however there are risks. First of all, you may not like the plan that you thought you would like when buying, or the rate may come back differently than you anticipated. Then you've got to go through the process again. During any time that you do not have insurance, if anything happens, it will not be covered. Then the condition may fall into the pre-existing condition category, such that you are responsible for all expenses until a certain time. Or worse, you could have a serious medical problem and then cannot get medically underwritten insurance at all.

Cancel Existing Insurance

You can let your insurance lapse by not paying for it, but if you're on a plan that automatically takes the payment from your account, they'll keep taking your money until you cancel with them. Since the mail can be slow and uncertain, and since the company may not be entirely high-tech, your best bet is to call the customer service telephone number, tell them you wish to cancel, and then fax a signed letter to the fax number that they give you. You'll want to follow up on this fax a day or two later to make sure that the information has been entered correctly, especially the termination date. Many companies will not provide a partial month of coverage, so the best time to cancel/start insurance is at the end/beginning of a month. If you must do it at another time of the month, then you'll probably end up without coverage for part of the month or paying for overlapping dates of coverage.

Summary

Congratulations, you've done it! For further tips on avoiding rip-offs, read on to the next chapter.

Chapter 10

Don't Get Ripped-Off

Nobody likes to get ripped-off. I don't know what's worse: being deceived, the feeling of not being able to see through the deceptions, or loosing money. You may not even realize you're getting ripped-off when you pay for benefits that you're not using. Here are a bunch of tips that I've found that may help you to avoid rip-offs. I've even included a story about how my family was significantly ripped-off by an unlicensed plan at the end of this chapter so that you can avoid this increasingly common danger.

Rip-Offs When Buying Health Insurance

Many rip-offs can occur when you are buying health insurance and then once you've got health insurance. This section has the rip-offs that can happen when you're buying insurance, and the following section has the rip-offs that can occur once you've got the insurance and you are using it.

⚠ Don't Buy a "Plan" – Buy Insurance

Check with your state department of insurance to make sure that the company is licensed to sell health insurance: individual or small group as you have selected. The company might be licensed for one but not the other. Unlicensed companies may exist only to collect premiums from you, and may be unwilling or unable to pay claims. If they are unable to pay claims, then you will be held responsible for all your charges, since any state health insurance guaranty trust will not pay for those claims. If you are unable to pay the claims, then you could end up in bankruptcy.

The NAIC lists names of companies who have intentionally or unintentionally been involved in the sale or promotion of unlicensed insurance. Sometimes reputable agents can be drawn in by one of these scams, so be sure that the state lists the insurer as valid, and your agent as a representative for the insurer.

> 💡 For a list of names that have been discovered to be involved in unlicensed activity and received government action, see the website : www.naic.org/consumer_rsp_state_enforcement.htm

⚠ All Quotes / Rates are Not Created Equally

Some plans have extremely "tight" ratings structures that would mean a higher rate for the smallest condition. Others may have a "looser" structure that would not increase the rate for the same condition. So when making your choice, keep in mind that the qualitative assessment around the numbers can make a big difference. Although in most cases the rate quoted is the one that an applicant will receive, the rate structure can be manipulated such that the quoted rate is not the rate that most people receive. Consider Figure 8.1 again. If the rate quoted was still the one most likely to be given to insureds, but the first rate was removed, and the amount added to the other rates to the right of the Quoted Rate, an insurer could still quote the most likely rate, just as long as that number was higher than any other group of rates. An extreme example is 21%, 20%, 20%, 20%, 19% – a grouping that would match the criteria but also put as many people as possible into a higher rating group, shown in Figure 10.1 (compare to Figure 8.1 for one that might be more fair).

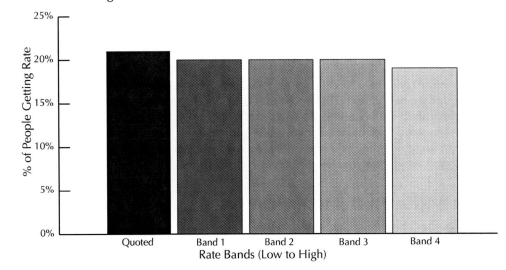

Figure 10.1: Fictional Unfavorable Rating Structure

⚠ Guarantee Issue Doesn't Mean Guaranteed Affordable

The company is going to guarantee that they will issue a policy to you, but if you have an existing medical condition, they are going to know how much they're going to spend on your condition over time – and charge you for it. You may spend less money paying for insurance than you might spend on medical bills without insurance. If there is no medical underwriting involved, such as in states with community rating, then everybody pays the same amount regardless if they have a medical condition.

⚠ Guaranteed Renewable Doesn't Mean Guaranteed Affordable

Even though most policies provide guaranteed renewable coverage, you should still check to make sure that the insurance is guaranteed renewable, even though they're all supposed to be guaranteed renewable as part of the HIPAA law. However, even if it is guaranteed re-newable doesn't mean that the premiums will continue to be the same. Yes, the premiums are likely to go up as the cost of healthcare goes up and as you get older for individual plans. But some plans are more likely to experience jumps in rates from year to year, or even in-between yearly increases. This could mean that two companies with similar rates at the beginning could have very different increases at the end of the first and second years of the insurance policy, resulting in very different premiums a few years after inception. This is par-ticularly noticeable if your insurance includes an unhealthy group, such as when you buy a small employer plan with an unhealthy group, or an association group plan that is open to everyone. Keep in mind that small business group plan rates may be more regulated in the amount that they can increase premiums, as opposed to association group plans that may not have any regulation in how much they can increase the annual premiums.

⚠ Beware the Re-Underwriter

Though illegal in many states, and currently out of fashion with insurance companies, re-underwriting, which is changing the rate on the policy when you get sick after you've had the insurance for some time, is still possible in some places. Check with your state to find out if it is possible in your state, and check the news sources for your prospective insurers to see if they have any history of this approach. If your state does not specifically prohibit re-underwriting of health insurance (also known as post-claims underwriting), then you may want to be cautious about insuring with a company that has a history of this practice. In 2002, the Wall Street Journal ran articles on this practice by some out of state association plans. The Florida courts intervened and made changes. You need to know the laws in your state.

⚠ Check the Newspapers for Reports About Your Prospective Insurer

While every insurer can hit a foul ball every once in a while, you may discover that some of them are always having problems, and others are never mentioned in the newspapers. A quick check, either using the reference desk at your local library, or an online newspaper search engine, will tell you whether the insurer is a wolf in sheep's clothing. For example, newspaper reports have included information about lawsuits against insurers, actions by state governments, and reports of inadequate coverage sold by insurers. You can also find reports by individuals on discussion boards, but be aware that sometimes negative reports and comments can be posted by the competition in a smear campaign.

⚠ Sales Pressure

Insurance Agents are sales professionals. They make money when they sell an insurance product. They are trained in the features of health insurance and in the sales process, including ways to influence the closing of a sale. The degree to which they use certain approaches, such as high-pressure sales tactics varies. One agent who represented only one insurer came to my house and started writing up the application before even asking for my decision. This was uncomfortable, although he backed down a little when I told him very directly that we would not file an application until we had finished getting information from all insurers. Trust your instincts, and do ask your family, friends, and acquaintances for names of independent agents that have helped them. I was able to find a personable agent through the local chamber of commerce who really understands the available products and did not use sales pressure to try to close the sale. Also know that people working directly for the insurer are sales representatives: insurance agents who are employed by the insurer.

⚠ Check on Your Agent

You can check with your state agency responsible for insurance to determine if an agent is currently licensed to sell health insurance, and also which insurance companies they are licensed to represent. The state government will also have a record of any disciplinary actions against that agent. If the person selling you the product says that they don't need a license, or that they have a way to get around the expense and red tape of insurance, look elsewhere.

⚠ Make Checks/Payments Out to Insurer not Agent/Third Party

Don't pay cash or make a check out to your agent or a third party. Only make out a check in the name of a licensed insurance company, and make sure that all paperwork also includes the same licensed company name. You want to make sure that your money goes towards the policy, otherwise your insurance would not be valid for non-payment. Don't sign any blank forms either!

⚠ Know about Pre-Existing Conditions and How Plans Deal with Them

This is really important if you have any medical condition. You'll want to know if credit for any existing health insurance coverage will apply, and how long you may have to wait for coverage. You may also want to make sure that you are not given an "exclusionary rider" for a condition for which you desire coverage. Most plans consider pregnancy a pre-existing condition and will not cover the pregnancy, but they should probably cover the baby! At extra expense, of course.

⚠ Choose Quality, Not Price

A good plan won't rip you off, but it may cost more. The cheapest may not be the best, and of course the most expensive may not be either. A good company will provide a good product and stand behind the offering, paying claims when they occur. You need to be concerned with how your coverage will work if you get sick, especially since once you're sick, getting different coverage can be more work and potentially much more expensive.

⚠ If You Get Sick, Buying Health Insurance Can Be Difficult and Expensive Even If You Already Have Health Insurance

You've seen it elsewhere in this book, but it really bears repeating here: get the right health insurance when you are at your healthiest. Once you're sick, it can be more difficult to find an insurer and get a good deal. There's no real "credit" for having had health insurance previously, other than that sometimes you can get coverage when otherwise you might not (through HIPAA at the end of your COBRA), and shorter periods (but not lower rates) for pre-existing condition waiting periods. Switching insurers means that you are likely to go through medical underwriting in most states. The insurers use this underwriting to set the rates that you will pay. It can be more expensive once you're sick.

Years ago when I applied for life insurance, I asked and found out that I was a few pounds too heavy to get the best rate. I managed to loose those few pounds, and when we bought our health insurance, we got the best rate from the insurer. We've got the plan that is right for us, and we'll continue to get this best rate as long as we keep paying our premiums and don't move out of the area. Even if a family member gets sick. Granted, the main reason for doing everything you can to stay healthy is not solely to get the best rate.

⚠ Shop Around

If you don't take the time to shop around for quotes, then you may end up paying more or getting fewer benefits than you need. It will take some time to shop around and then compare the rates, but every $100 of monthly savings is $1,200 a year plus interest on the money that you save. Know also the rate from an insurer will be the same from every agent or directly from the insurer.

⚠ Don't Get Stuck As Part of an Unhealthy Group

How would you know if you are part of an unhealthy group? You may find out only because the rates are high, or are getting significantly higher over time (higher than the typical annual increase in the 8–10% range). You might also become part of an unhealthy group as part of a group plan where the healthier people leave the group, with the less healthy staying in the plan because they can't get other options. This may start out with a lower first year rate, and significant increases in rates in years after. This has been shown to happen with groups that allow anyone to join because they seem to be magnets for less healthy people. While initially it may provide lower rates for everyone, rates will go up, and you can become stranded in this group due to a health event. It's best to have control over who is in your "group", and if you don't have a group, consider the individual options where you receive a policy and not a certificate of coverage from the insurer.

⚠ Don't Ever Get Denied Health Insurance

If you apply for insurance, and get denied, this is a black mark that you will always carry with you. Subsequent insurers will want to know if and when you were denied, and they might possibly use this information to either deny you coverage or raise the rates that you pay. There's no use lying about it. They can cancel your insurance for that too, because they'll know from the Medical Information Bureau what you've said previously. Plus they almost always state in the application that they can go to your doctors for information, too.

⚠ Going Without Coverage Can Cost More

I've read recently about people with respectable incomes and medical problems who have decided that they cannot afford health insurance. Don't let this happen to you. Explore all your options about where to get insurance, and make it a priority. Financially speaking, if you can get health insurance any way, it's probably better than doing without. For example, let's say you've got a condition that is likely to cost $40,000 over the next year, but you lost your job at an employer with more than 20 employees because you can't work, and the COBRA payment is $1200 a month. Your COBRA payments are going to be $14,400 for the next year, as opposed to $40,000. You may be able to negotiate with the provider to reduce the $40,000, but you're not going to get it less than $14,400. Lots of things can happen in the next year including regaining employment. If you can find a way to finance the amount (family, friends, home equity, sale of other assets), or can get a job with benefits or a spouse can get a job with benefits, you'll be in a better position to avoid a bankruptcy because of the medical problems.

> Most people know how a credit bureau keeps information about your financial affairs and that the information can affect the interest rates that you pay. However, most people do not know about the Medical Information Bureau (MIB). Information about your individually underwritten life, health, disability, and long term care insurance applications and policies is stored at this consumer reporting agency for about seven years. This information can affect your rate every time you apply for subsequent life, health, disability, and long term care insurance. According to a study by Milliman Actuarial Consultants, 80% of healthcare costs are due to 15% of the insured people. The MIB can be used to find those 15% and increase their rates or deny them coverage.

Now let's say you go the typical 18-months offered by the COBRA law, and then you convert to a HIPAA guaranteed plan at $1500 a month. That's still cheaper than a $40,000 a year in bills, and you still have the option to pick up insurance in other ways.

There's no perfect single solution for everyone. Employers with less than 20 employees don't have to offer a COBRA coverage, except in some states, like Georgia where they have to give a 3 month COBRA-like coverage regardless of employer size. If the employer goes out of business or cancels insurance completely, you may not have many options unless your insurer or state has a conversion to an individual policy.

⚠ Some States Have Better Plans and Costs Than Others

Since health insurance is regulated at the state level, you'll find different laws and opportunities in different states. When you look at what is available in your state, and if you don't like your options, you may find that the grass is greener elsewhere. My family used to live in New Jersey, and for a healthy family, the rates can take up a very large amount of money each month (over $800) due to a number of reasons. I thought about what it would be like to live elsewhere, and found out that in Maryland we could get less coverage, which is what we needed, for only a few hundred dollars a month. A few years later we moved to North Carolina, and find that the laws and the products here are also good for us, so that we can manage to keep health insurance as a healthy family.

⚠ Be Careful Whom You Ask About Health Plans

While your friends and family may have your best interests at heart, they may not know enough about health insurance and any particular insurance company to provide good input. For example, someone who may have excellent coverage with an insurance company may not see it as such when they are going through a medical event and must pay a relatively low out-of-pocket cost and may complain about the company. Since they do not have perspective across many policies and companies, their input may mislead you. Doctors offices may provide some good information about the insurance companies that refuse more claims, but that could also be because the doctors office has a hard time filing the claims correctly or is trying to bill additional services that are not covered. A provider may also direct you to a plan that pays more to them, not necessarily one the has better benefits for your well being. So when doing your research, look at the numbers, look into what your state agency for insurance has to offer, and look at the news, not just what your friends, family, and doctors have to say.

⚠ You're Always Comparing Apples to Oranges

Unless you are comparing different deductible, coinsurance, and copayments for the same insurance plan, you are comparing apples to oranges. Every plan will cover things that another will not. Some will deny more claims than others. Some will give you greater value for a copayment than others. A copayment may represent much greater value than just the doctor's fee.

For example, let's say you went to a dermatologist for a skin cancer screening, and the dermatologist found something that needed to be sent to the lab for testing. In a copayment plan, you might pay more to see this specialist than your regular doctor. But your copayment is more likely to cover the doctor's time, the removal of the questionable skin, and the lab work to find out that the growth is benign. If you don't have a copayment, then you're going to be responsible for the doctor's time, the procedure to remove the skin, plus the lab fees for testing the skin. If you are in a network, you'll get discounts, but you will still be paying for the items at the discounted rate until you've reached your deductible, before any benefits are available to you. It is difficult to compare health insurance, but using the spreadsheet in Chapter 8 to help calculate the numbers and using public information to assess the quality of the insurer, you can make the comparison a lot easier. With these techniques it's more like comparing one variety of apple to another.

Rip-Offs When Using Your Health Insurance

Watch out for these rip-offs and issues once you've got health insurance and when you're using it.

⚠ Check the Policy When You Get It

Make sure that you understand what is and is not covered. Depending on the law in your state, you only have a few days to weeks to read the policy and return it to get a refund of your payment. Everything that you may have read or heard from an agent prior to receipt of the policy may be incorrect, and

> ⚲ "One man came to us - he thought he had a good plan. He has $70,000 in bills because he didn't realize he didn't have comprehensive health insurance."
> -Beth B. Parrott, Owner, Parrott Insurance and Benefits

the application or policy probably states this. If you need help getting through the policy, ask your agent to review it with you for specific conditions or exclusions. It's too late to review the policy when months or years have gone by and you make a claim that is excluded by the policy, and you wish that the claim was not excluded.

⚠ You Can Usually Increase Your Deductible Without Re-Underwriting, But Not Always Reduce It.

Since this means that you'd be likely to lower your monthly payment for health insurance, it is counter-intuitive. You'd think that the insurance company would want more money from you, but apparently they've found that people who become sick want smaller deductibles, certainly an advantage when your medical bills become large and ongoing.

⚠ If You Have a Network, Make Sure You Use Doctors in Network

Use the doctors and facilities in your network, otherwise, even if you have out-of-network coverage, you may end up paying more for similar services, and may find that services may exceed the reasonable and customary amounts. Certain services may not be covered at all, since the provider may not be aware of what is and is not covered in your plan. They may make choices that will be more expensive for you, even though

> ⚲ "Always always no matter what is going on save all your medical receipts because you never know when that medical disaster is going to hit and there may be able to write it off against your taxes: copayments, prescriptions, anything that you're buying related to treatments."
> -Lauren Gadkowski Lindsay, CFP®, NAPFA Registered Financial Advisor, Personal Financial Advisors

they may not be medically superior to what your plan covers. Remember that doctors are not in the business of health insurance.

⚠ Use the State Department of Insurance to Your Advantage

If you have any problems, and cannot resolve them with your insurance company, contact your state's department of insurance. You may find that if you are getting insurance through an out-of-state association that your state does not have enough power to resolve issues, and that the state in which the association is based also does not have the teeth to resolve problems. You can also go to the state department of insurance if your insurer goes out of business. There is probably a state guarantee association that will cover bills when a legal licensed insurer cannot pay bills. If your insurer is not licensed or in-state, then they won't be able to help you. You should also check out all of the agents that you may talk to during your search. You want to make sure that they are legitimate and don't have a history of problems.

⚠ Beware of Reasonable and Customary Charges, Services Not Covered by Your Insurer, and Daily Maximums

There are limits on how much a plan will pay for certain services that will leave you with the rest of the bill. There may be an upper dollar limit that they will pay towards a particular procedure, and a doctor that charges more than this will expect you to pay for the difference. This isn't so much the case when you are seeing a doctor in a network, although a separate problem of services provided that are not covered can come up. If you see a network doctor, you can ask about whether certain services are covered, and also check with the insurer prior to undergoing procedures to find out what is covered. Some insurers will require pre-certification of procedures and some also have a program that works with you and your doctor to make sure that only necessary services are performed so that neither you or the insurer are liable for excess charges. Also watch out for daily maximums that may mean that you are underinsured if you end up in a hospital for a serious problem or reasonable and customary charges for a procedure that are much less than your non-network provider charges.

⚠ Make Sure the Insurer Pays Your Claims

Whether the insurer is reimbursing you, or paying directly to the provider, make sure that they are paying, and that they are not denying claims or taking more than a few months to pay. The provider will come to you with the bill to get payment, and if you're not in a network, you'll have to pay, work out a payment plan, and possibly find a way to finance the charges for the period of time until the insurer reimburses you.

⚠ Make Sure That The Premium is Paid

If you've got an individual plan, or pay for association group coverage directly to the insurer, then you have total control and responsibility to make sure that the payment arrives at the insurer or you could end up without insurance. But what happens if your employer pays for the insurance or you pay money to an association or union for healthcare coverage? How do you know if they are paying and what happens if they don't?

> ☼ "A lot of times the employee doesn't know that this has happened until they go to use their health insurance and the claim is denied. There are no conversion options - they're stuck. They have to go out and find their own. It's a legal issue and they need an attorney."
> -Beth B. Parrott, Owner, Parrott Insurance and Benefits

There are few checks and balances in place to handle situations like these. You are likely to have a hard time if this happens. First of all, both the policy owner and the agent that sold the policy will be sent delinquency notices. The agent will certainly try to ensure that the payment is made. Secondly, people using the policy will start to see that claims are going unpaid. Unless those covered on the plan are also responsible for paying the insurer, they will not know that something is happening until the claims go unpaid. A competent attorney should be sought if this happens.

⚠ Check Your Explanation of Benefits Forms

There are two reasons to check your Explanation of Benefits (EOB) forms when they arrive. The first is to see how much the insurance company is paying and how much you will owe. Hopefully everything came out right, but sometimes the provider will use the incorrect billing codes, and the insurer won't pay the proper amount. The remedy here is to check with the provider, who may be able to re-file the bill correctly. You can also learn a lot about how much a procedure would cost without insurance or outside of a network.

The second reason to check your EOB's is to make sure that the provider is billing properly and that no false claims are being filed against your policy. You want to make sure that the provider is not filing claims for procedures that were not performed. This could in turn drive up your insurance rates, put untrue medical conditions on your file, or further involve you in criminal acts of insurance fraud.

Your provider may also send you a statement showing what was billed to your insurance, what you have paid, how much your insurance has paid, how much is owed (from you and/or the insurer), and how much the fees were discounted.

⚠ Keep Your Health Insurance Card and Numbers Private

Don't give out your health insurance number or card to anyone to whom you wouldn't give your credit card information. There are scams such as free tests and screenings that might take your information and involve you somehow in an insurance rip-off scam. Many insurers are moving away from using your social security number as your ID number, however, the number is still just as important to protect. Your health insurance card and its information are part of your identity.

⚠ Be Careful About Moving

If you move, depending where you move and how far it is from your current residence, you may lose coverage or get a rate change. You may also be subject to underwriting again, even if you stay within the same state. Perhaps it is worth reconsidering a move, or at least maintaining your residence in your current locale, if you do not have health insurance lined up at your destination. Check with your insurer to find out what the restrictions are on residence location with your current health insurance policy. If you have a medical condition and plan to buy individual health insurance, states with community rating will have lower rates for those with medical conditions. Conversely, states without community rating may have lower rates for those that are healthy.

> 🔎 "There's a new trend: to keep a product in many states, where you can move from state to state, without re-underwritng, but rating for costs locally."
> -Bob Hurley, Senior Vice President of Carrier Relations, eHealthInsurance.com

If you are planning a move, you may want to get some quotes to know what health insurance costs may be like in your new location. Even if you are moving due to a job change and are planning on taking the employer group health insurance, if you at some time quit, lose the job, or the employer goes out of business, you will need to buy individual insurance or go on COBRA.

⚠ **Jurisdictional No Mans Land**

If you get insurance from an out of state association, then the master policy is written to that association in the association's state. If you then encounter a problem and contact your state department of insurance, you may find that they cannot help you, or help you well, because of the out of state association. If you then contact the department of insurance in the state of the association, you may find that they cannot fully help you because you are not a resident of the state and they are unfamiliar with laws in your state. You may find that neither department of insurance can resolve problems to your satisfaction.

⚠ **Insurer Wants to Cancel**

If your insurer notifies you that they wish to cancel your policy, especially just after you begin to use the benefits, you should contact your state department of insurance. You have certain rights based on the laws in your states. You may also wish to obtain legal counsel from a qualified attorney familiar with health insurance.

My Experience with a Health Insurance Scam

When I was working at a startup company, the company proceeded to close, and those who were still working and on the health plan or those who were on COBRA continuation of the health plan were brought together to receive information about their options. Since the company was closing, all benefit plans would no longer exist. That meant that the COBRA continuation option also would not be available.

The insurance agent who was working with the company management provided the basic options for the New Jersey plans and offered coverage through the same insurance company as the employer had for the group plan, but as an individual plan. He also offered a "benefit plan", which he clearly repeated was not insurance, but shared many of the same attributes as the individual health insurance, and got around those troublesome insurance regulations. He probably mentioned the ERISA law that exempts self insured employers from some state regulations.

The health benefit plan paperwork required that the enrollee sign a statement that they would become an "employee" of the benefit company, be required to attempt to make sales calls of the company's products for a certain number of hours a week (wink, wink), and only be paid for successful sales. Since this benefit plan was significantly less expensive than the health insurance option, and they claimed that it was "creditable coverage," so other health insurance/plans would not see any gap in coverage, we decided to give it a try.

We mailed our checks for coverage, and went about the normal process of living our lives and raising two young children. When it came time for doctor's visits, we were responsible for filing paperwork with the plan. OK, well I guess we needed to do this filing because of the lower cost. We received reimbursement for the payments, but not for the full amount. Errors were made. Even when we found other coverage, and requested cancellation, our check for the next months amount was not returned.

This "benefit plan" acted like an insurance plan, until it was time to submit and receive reimbursement for claims. At one point, my wife got sick while on vacation. She called the number on her insurance card to find a doctor in the local area whose charges would be covered by the plan. The plan representative gave her a name and number of a doctor. She made an appointment and went to see the doctor. However, when checking out she was told that the doctor's office did not work with her benefit company and that she would have to pay the full amount and send the claim to her benefits company for reimbursement. A little surprised and shocked, she paid for the services on a credit card. When feeling a little better, she took this claim up with the benefit company, only to be told that the doctor was not part of the plan. She explained what had happened to this representative only to be told that there was nothing they could do. Not happy with this answer, over the next year she continued to fight with the benefit company to pay the bill. Over a year later, the benefit company sent a check to the doctors office who held on to it until she happened to call and they then forwarded it to us. The whole process took about 18 months to resolve. Although this "benefit plan" resembled other insurance plans, the application process and the claims process where highly questionable and should have raised red flags for us.

At the time, there were around 28 sham insurers that had been identified, according to the U.S. General Accounting Office. Our particular plan has been mentioned in newspapers, court documents, and the leaders of the group were charged with criminal offenses. We had the second best outcome other than not getting taken in by the scam in the first place: nobody got seriously ill while on the plan, and we were back with a real licensed insurer after only a few months on the sham plan, and the people in charge of the company are in jail.

Real Life Scenarios

Hopefully by learning about some of the problems that people have faced in real life, and a few that are possibilities based on circumstances similar to real life stories, you can learn enough to avoid problems that can end in financial ruin: life savings spent, and no end of medical expenses in sight.

These are presented as fictionalized stories that start with a person to be insured that has a serious medical condition. They include possible steps that could be taken for the person with the medical condition and also for family members that are healthy. Check with your agent and other financial professionals to see if any of these ideas will work for you.

Problems presented here are primarily caused by not knowing the cracks in the health insurance system, and occasionally due to giving health insurance spending a low priority, including saving money for an emergency fund, or just plain not having enough money (if this is you, check for eligibility for government programs). Of course, not having health insurance in the first place can mean that you are responsible for any costs, and at worst don't get care at all, with potentially fatal consequences.

It's useful to know some of the medical conditions that are deemed serious enough to cause rejection or a higher rate when applying for health insurance. You may wish to refer to the chart on page 30 in Chapter 2 that shows a number of conditions that might have such an effect, of course with the exception of those states that offer guaranteed issue and community rating.

The Family Breadwinner Gets Sick and Cannot Continue to Work

The Family Has Health Insurance as Part of the Employer Group.

- The family pays for the COBRA extension until the working spouse is able to add the family to the spouse's large employer's group policy at work during the next "open season" opportunity to do so. Example costs are $1,200 a month for COBRA, and then $400 for the employee contribution to a health plan.

- The family pays for the COBRA extension until the working spouse is able to add the family to the spouse's small employer's group policy at work during the next "open season" opportunity to do so. The next year health insurance is dropped by the company due to the significant cost increase brought about by the illness, and the family is able to purchase individual health insurance for the health family members, and finds it difficult to find and expensive to buy health insurance for the person with the medical condition because they don't live in a state with community rating/guaranteed issue. Example costs are $1,200 a month for COBRA, and then $500 for the employee contribution to a health plan, $300 a month for private health insurance for the healthy family members, and $1000 a month for private health insurance for the person with the medical condition.

- The family pays for the COBRA extension until it ends (29 months due to disability), then converts the breadwinner to an individual HIPAA guaranteed plan, with the healthy family members taking individual health insurance. Example costs are $1,200 a month for COBRA, and then $1,500 a month for HIPAA guaranteed for the whole family.

- The family pays for the COBRA extension until the spouse is able to find employment at a large employer and the waiting period for employer health insurance is satisfied. The family then pays whatever contribution is required by the new employer for health insurance. Example costs are $1,200 a month for COBRA, and then $400 a month for the employee contribution to a health plan.

- The family pays for the COBRA extension until the spouse is able to find employment at a small employer and the waiting period for employer health insurance is satisfied. The family then pays whatever contribution is required by the new employer for the health insurance. The small employer then stops providing health insurance at renewal because of the massive costs incurred by the person with a medical condition. The family then must find other insurance options. Example costs are $1,200 a month for COBRA, then $500 a month for the employee contribution to a health plan.

- The family pays for the COBRA extension until it ends, and applies for Medicare for the disabled person and takes individual health insurance for the healthy family members. Medicare is approved, but Medicare isn't as comprehensive as many private insurance plans, so more expenses need to be paid out-of-pocket, along with the deductible and copayments for Medicare.

- The family pays for the COBRA extension, but finds the costs too high to pay every month, misses payments, and looses coverage. The family, who doesn't live in a state with community rating/guaranteed issue, purchases individual health insurance for the healthy family members, but finds that coverage cannot be obtained from most private health insurers for the person with a medical condition. Health insurers willing to take the person with the medical condition charge a lot more because of the existing condition. Example costs are $1,200 a month for COBRA, $300 a month for the individual insurance for the healthy family members, and $1000 a month for the person with the medical condition.

- The family pays for the COBRA extension, but finds the costs too high to pay every month, misses payments, and looses coverage. The family, who lives in a state with community rating/guaranteed issue, looks at buying family health insurance, and finds it also very expensive, but the whole family can be covered without any medical underwriting. Example costs are $1,200 a month for COBRA, $1000 a month for a family regardless of health status.

- The family takes the COBRA extension, but decides to move to another state that has community rating/guaranteed issue and buys a family health insurance policy. Example costs are $1,200 a month for COBRA, $1000 a month for a family regardless of health status.

- Since the two adults in the family have never been married, the family immediately has a simple marriage. Since it is a marriage, the family pays for the COBRA extension only until the working spouse is able to add the family to the large employer's group policy at work nearly immediately for the reason of marriage. Example costs are $1,200 a month for COBRA, and then $400 for the employee contribution to a health plan.

The Family Has Individual Health Insurance for the Family.

- The family keeps the individual health insurance and doesn't have any premium increases for the insurance due to the medical condition. However, since the family took a large deductible for the health insurance policy, then now have an additional deductible to pay each year for medical care before insurance pays. Example costs are $300 a month for a family in a state without community rating, and $1000 a month for a family in a state with community rating.

- The family keeps the individual health insurance and doesn't have any premium increases for the insurance due to the medical condition. Since the family took a rather low deductible and coinsurance, the financial strain due to the illness is contained as the insurance starts paying right away. Example costs are $600 a month for a family in a state without community rating, and $1000 a month for a family in a state with community rating.

- The family keeps the individual health insurance and doesn't have any premium increases for the insurance due to the medical condition. Since the family took a rather low deductible and coinsurance, the financial strain due to the illness is contained as the insurance starts paying right away. However, the family decides to move to be closer to extended family and finds that their insurance cannot be taken to the new location. Fortunately they found this out before moving, and can stay in their current location and keep their existing insurance. Example costs are $600 a month for a family in a state without community rating, and $1000 a month for a family in a state with community rating.

- The family keeps their insurance, an indemnity plan which has an 80/20 split on all expenses, and doesn't see increases in premium because of the medical condition. However, since treatment costs were $200,000 in the first year, and projected to be high for a number of years, the family will need to pay the $40,000 share for the first year, along with additional coinsurance amounts for years to come. The family sold their house and moved into a low-cost dwelling to pay for part of the expenses, and applied for Medicaid once all assets were gone. Example costs are $1000 a month for health insurance.

- The family keeps their insurance, a plan with an annual maximum of $100,000 and a lifetime maximum of $1,000,000, and doesn't see increases in premium because of the medical condition. However, treatment costs were $200,000 in the first year, and projected to be significant for years to come, the family will need to pay their deductible/coinsurance amount of $5,000 for the first year, plus expenses that exceed the $100,000 limit: another $100,000 dollars. The family sold everything to pay for the bills and still ended up in bankruptcy and applied for Medicaid. Example costs are $300 a month for health insurance.

The Family Has Association Health Insurance for the Family.

- The family, which lives in a state without community rating, keeps the association health insurance and doesn't have any premium increases for the insurance due to the medical condition. Since the family took a rather low deductible and coinsurance, the financial strain due to the illness is contained as the insurance starts paying right away. The first renewal year after the medical event, the premium increases are huge. The family hangs onto the insurance for the next year, and finds that the next premium increase is also huge and they cannot afford to continue on the plan. There are no conversion options for association group plans, so the family must look for individual insurance, which is difficult to find if you have a medical condition. The family cannot find anything that saves them any money over the association plan, and sticks with it. The increases continue, and finally the group in which they are insured is cancelled, and the family must find individual insurance for the healthy members, and anything they can for the person with the medical condition. Example costs are $400 a month for the first years premium, an increase of 25% after the first year, with increases in this range year after year as the association group to which they belong loses the healthy people and expenses for those with medical conditions are paid out, resulting in a high number of claims and the justification to raise the rate.

What Should I Do When...

This section gives some ideas as to what you might do when certain life events happen. There may be a number of choices in a given situation which may not all be included here. For the options listed, steps are presented that can be taken to minimize negative financial consequences. Check with your agent or advisors to see if these will work for you.

A Child With a Medical Condition is Too Old to Continue on Parents Plan

Parents Plan Has a Conversion Option

- Determine if conversion policy would be comparable in rate and features to open market individual policy. Purchase the better deal using techniques in this book.

Parent Plan Has No Conversion Option

- Purchase individual insurance on open market, subject to increased rate.
- Look into group health insurance from the child's employer.
- Determine if condition would be eligible for Medicare.
- Hire child into your own small business, and put the child on your group policy.

I Want to Retire Early

The Family Has Health Insurance as Part of the Employer Group.

- Research costs of individual plans for a combined family and separately for family members that have medical conditions. Consider getting the policy issued in the younger spouse's name, with any children on that policy, so the older spouse may more easily shift to Medicare without affecting the policy.

- Determine cost of COBRA from the employer, and whether any early retirement health benefits are available and how much they will cost. Ensure that the commitment of coverage and rate is in writing, and consider the long-term prospects of the employing company. If no company, no coverage.

- If significant medical condition, determine COBRA costs, and HIPAA guaranteed policy costs.

- If significant medical condition, consider moving to a state with community rating and guaranteed issue.

I Am Young and Healthy and Want to Leave My Employer

The Family has Health Insurance as part of the Employer Group.

- Determine best deal for you on open market when leaving employment. You have 60 days to answer whether you want COBRA from the employer, if employer is subject to COBRA. If employer not subject to COBRA, do search for individual policy prior to quitting.

The Family has Individual Health Insurance.

- Make sure that you are getting the best deal on your health insurance.

I've Just Been Let Go from My Employer.

The Family has Health Insurance as Part of the Employer Group.

- Determine best deal for you on open market when leaving employment. You have 60 days to answer whether you want COBRA from the employer, if employer is subject to COBRA. If employer not subject to COBRA, do search immediately to prevent any serious gaps in coverage. Consider a short-term policy for the period of time before you get insurance – remember if you get sick on short-term policy, you might pay more or be denied for regular health insurance. If you have a medical condition, then the COBRA to HIPAA option may be your only option: an expensive one.

The Family has Individual Health Insurance.

- Make sure that you are getting the best deal on your health insurance.

I Am Going Through a Divorce and Will No Longer Have Health Insurance from My Spouse

The Family Has Health Insurance as Part of the Employer Group.

- COBRA rules apply to divorcing spouses and dependents. Contact a lawyer to ensure payment of health insurance is part of divorce negotiations. Payment of COBRA fees may be pricey. If you don't have a health condition, start shopping for individual insurance.

If rates are too high or coverage is unavailable due to a medical condition, consider employment group insurance for yourself. Other possibilities are moving to a state with community rating, deferring divorce (a prolonged separation), re-marriage, and government programs if you have few assets.

The Family Has Individual Health Insurance or Individual Purchase of Association Group Insurance.

- If your state or individual insurance policy has a provision for divorce, then you may be able to obtain a separate policy. Consider moving those without medical conditions to their own individual policies and leaving the remaining person(s) on the existing policy to prevent medical underwriting from raising the rates. Consider having the combined policy managed by an impartial third party in order to ensure continued coverage without higher rates from medical underwriting.

The Family Has Health Insurance as Part of Your Own Company.

- If have a medical condition, consider the four types of health insurance coverage and how many you can qualify to get. Worst case is to get coverage as part of the settlement to continue with the company. Beware that many things can happen to a small business, including sale, bankruptcy, and closing, so continuation of coverage is questionable unless proper legal maneuvers are made. Check with a qualified attorney.

I Have a Medical Condition and I Don't Know if I'll be Declined or Upcharged

- Call a qualified health insurance agent (NAHU/AHIA member) and ask. You'll probably get an idea of which insurers will offer coverage, and what level of surcharge you may face. You can also refer to the tables of conditions in Chapter 2.

Summary

I'm sure that there are more rip-offs and scenarios out there, but these are the big ones. Please check our website for updates and contribute your rip-offs, stories, questions, and ideas at www.BestHealthInsuranceBook.com.

Appendix A

National Resources

Here is a list of national resources: organizations and their websites. Included with each entry is a brief description of what you may find at the website or how the organization may help you find the right health insurance and the best deal.

Essential Resources

www.BestHealthInsuranceBook.com

The book website. It contains downloads, updates to the book, articles, online resources, and more.

www.naic.org/state_web_map.htm

The National Association of Insurance Commissioners (NAIC), an association of the insurance commissioners of the U.S. states and territories, provides a map and links to each of the state insurance commission offices. Each state/territory maintains information about the insurance companies licensed to do business in that state, along with other helpful information for consumers, including complaints against companies.

www.naic.org/cis/index.do

The National Association of Insurance Commissioners (NAIC), an association of the insurance commissioners of the U.S. states and territories, has a Consumer Information Source that provides access to financial information about insurers, and consumer complaint information. The four reports that you should review for your state and the insurers in your state are the Complaint Counts by State, Complaint Counts by Code, Complaint Ratio Report (the most important), and the Complaint Trend Report (so you know if people are having fewer or more complaints over time).

www.nahu.org

The National Association of Health Underwriters (NAHU) provides important information to insurance agents who are actively working in health insurance, as well as to consumers. You can use this website to find an agent locally, though they are chosen at random from all possible agents to prevent people from creating mailing lists of health insurance agents. Also extremely valuable on this website is the Health Care Coverage Database that provides information about the laws in your state.

www.ahia.net

The Association of Health Insurance Advisors (AHIA) is a part of the National Association of Insurance and Financial Advisors. Like NAHU, serious health insurance agents join this association for information in their field. On this site you can find an agent and learn more about health insurance.

www.medicare.gov

This is the central Medicare information site with links and databases of all information necessary to understand, apply for, and use Medicare health benefits. This includes comprehensive lists of insurers in each state.

www.ncqa.org

The National Committee for Quality Assurance (NCQA) is an organization that compiles information supplied by managed care (HMO, POS, PPO) plans and creates a report card for insurers. If you are considering managed care options, see if they have a report card on the various insurers in your state.

www.jdpower.com/healthcare/

JD Power, the well known satisfaction survey company for automobiles, also has a section about healthcare and health insurance. See what surveyed people are saying about plans that you are considering.

www.consumerreports.com

A quick search of this website for "health insurance" will reveal free and pay articles that may be of interest, including articles related to member's reports of their satisfaction with particular insurer, and a ratings guide. Since there are so many insurers, and they vary by state, every insurer doesn't appear in the ratings, but this doesn't mean that they aren't any good, just not listed. The most important information from this site are the consumer ratings of how people felt about their insurer. Some of the other information is not detailed enough.

www.mib.com

The Medical Information Bureau will provide a free copy of the report that it may have on file for you due to your application for health and life insurance products. They will also let you know if they don't have a record for you. It takes a little work to make the request due to the need to prevent incorrect disclosure of information.

Additional Resources

www.healthfinder.gov

A U.S. Government run search engine that includes pre-screened health information. It also has a browse capability if you're not sure exactly how to search for what you need.

www.healthpartners.com/empower/costofcare/

HealthPartners is a private non-profit health insurance company in Minnesota that has a few web-tools that give useful information like an estimate of your annual healthcare costs, along with costs for some treatments by state. If you are insured by HealthPartners, you have access to even more information.

www.bcbsnc.com/apps/cost-estimator/

Blue Cross Blue Shield of North Carolina has a cost estimator for a number of medical services based on data gathered in North Carolina.

www.qualitycheck.org

This website gives you the ability to check on quality of the facilities that you are likely to use for the "big dollar" items discussed in Chapter 2.

www.healthdecisions.org

A resource provided by the America's Health Insurance Plans (AHIP) that provides a good list of companies by state and insurance type. For example, I found 35 companies in North Carolina listed for Health Insurance. There are web links to some of the companies where you can find more information and get quotes.

www.dol.gov/ebsa

The Employee Benefits Security Administration, part of the United States Department of Labor, provides consumer information about the various rules, regulations, and situations that you may encounter regarding health insurance. There are a number of consumer links and publications that provide helpful information when working through the terms and options available when leaving employment.

www.healthinsuranceinfo.net

Georgetown University has a Health Policy Institute that has written guides to health insurance in each individual state. The focus is on law and health policy in the state, and can serve as a guide to some of the laws, guarantees, and coverages required in any particular state. You should definitely get a copy for your state, and then check for updates anytime that you are considering changing health insurance.

www.ahrq.gov

The Agency for Healthcare Research and Quality provides information for consumers, as well as data that can be searched for healthcare cost information. Online healthcare cost information is available at www.BestHealthInsuranceBook.com that is based on data collected by this government agency.

www.napfa.org

Personal financial advisors who are members of the National Association on Personal Financial Advisors provide their services through fees, and not commissions on financial products. You can find an advisor here if you are in need of a comprehensive look at your personal financial situation, or need specific advice about insurance coverages, including health insurance.

Contributor Websites

Links to these websites can be found at www.BestHealthInsuranceBook.com, along with updates, online tools, and more.

www.jfsipp.com

Jennifer McLaurin, Director of Sales, John F. Sipp & Associates

www.parrottinsurance.com

Beth B. Parrott, Owner, Parrott Insurance and Benefits

Teresa Penninger, Individual Benefits Specialist, Parrott Insurance and Benefits

www.ehealthinsurance.com

Robert S. Hurley, Senior Vice President of Carrier Relations, eHealth Inc.

www.mypfa.com

Lauren Gadkowski Lindsay, CFP, NAPFA Registered Financial Advisor, Personal Financial Advisors

www.gewcpa.com

Marge Schiller, CFP, NAPFA Registered Financial Advisor, Goar, Endriss, and Walker, P.A.

Appendix B

State Resources

Information presented here provides you with the contact information for your state agency in charge of health insurance. In some cases a toll free number is provided that will work for in-state telephone calls. The state agency website can be useful in finding out changes in laws and additional details specific to your state. Where possible, Internet links are provided for Agency and Insurers. The Agency Search features are useful to check on whether a person is a licensed agent and whether any disciplinary action has occurred. Where present, links to lists or search features that provide a list of Health Insurers, including HMO's and PPO's is provided. However it is best to contact the state agency directly to confirm that any list is up-to-date, and for those that do not publish a list. Keep in mind that lists for individual insurers will likely differ from those that provide small group policies.

Frequently Agents are known as Producers when searching these resources. Also Health Insurance may be a separate item in some searches, and may be combined with Life in others because some states license Health and Life together. If they are combined, your best bet to find the list of insurers is to contact the state agency directly and let them know whether you are interested in individual or small group health insurers. The individual list is likely to include association group plans that are sold to individuals. You can also ask them to post the list to their website.

Please visit the website at www.BestHealthInsuranceBook.com for updates along with more resources.

Alabama
      Contact www.aldoi.gov/Consumers/
               334-241-4141
               ConsumerServices@insurance.alabama.gov

        Agent www.aldoi.gov/LicenseeSearch/

      Insurer www.aldoi.gov/CompanySearch/
               (Choose either 'HMO' or 'Non-Profit Health Care Service Plan Corp.' from "Type (Powers Held)" List, then click View for Company Details. "Click Here for Company Appointments" will list agents for that company)

Alaska
      Contact www.dced.state.ak.us/insurance/consumerinfo.htm
               907-269-7900
               insurance@commerce.state.ak.us

        Agent www.commerce.state.ak.us/insurance/apps/producersearch/InsLicStart.cfm

      Insurer www.dced.state.ak.us/insurance/pub/2005_Health_Information.pdf

Arizona
Contact www.id.state.az.us/consumer.html
800-325-2548
consumers@id.state.az.us

Agent app.az.gov/id/lookup/producersearch

Insurer www.id.state.az.us/publications/Report_on_AZ_Health_Insurers.pdf

Arkansas
Contact www.insurance.arkansas.gov/Consumers/divpage.htm
800-852-5494 / 501-271-2640
insurance.consumers@arkansas.gov

Agent www.insurance.arkansas.gov/is/agentsearch/agent.asp

Insurer www.insurance.arkansas.gov/is/companysearch/cosearch.asp

California
Contact www.insurance.ca.gov/0100-consumers/
800-927-4357 / 213-897-8921
Use online form for email

Agent www.insurance.arkansas.gov/is/companysearch/cosearch.asp

Insurer www.insurance.ca.gov/0100-consumers/hcpcarriers.cfm

Colorado
Contact www.dora.state.co.us/insurance/consumer/consumer.htm
800-930-3745
insurance@doa.state.co.us

Agent cdilookup.asisvcs.com/IndividualSearch.aspx

Insurer cdilookup.asisvcs.com/CompanySearch.aspx
www.dora.state.co.us/insurance/consumer/hlthcarrier.pdf
www.dora.state.co.us/insurance/consumer/smlgrplst(3-06).pdf

Connecticut
Contact www.ct.gov/cid/cwp/view.asp?a=1260&q=306846
800-203-3447 / 860-297-3900
ctinsdept.consumeraffairs@ct.gov

Agent www.catalog.state.ct.us/cid/License/licweb1.asp?cidNav=|

Insurer www.ct.gov/cid/cwp/view.asp?a=1267&q=254440
www.ct.gov/cid/cwp/view.asp?a=1267&q=254446

Delaware
Contact delawareinsurance.gov/departments/consumer/consumerhp.shtml
800-282-8611 / 302-674-7310
consumer@deins.state.de.us

Agent sbs-de-public.naic.org/producer_services.htm

Insurer delawareinsurance.gov/health/default.shtml#FAQ (top 10)
delawareinsurance.gov/departments/consumer/seilist.pdf

District of Columbia

Contact disr.dc.gov/disr/site/default.asp
202-727-8000
disb@dc.gov

Agent sbs-dc-public.naic.org/Lion-Web/jsp/sbsreports/AgentLookup.jsp

Florida

Contact www.fldfs.com/Consumers/index.htm
800-342-2762 / 850-413-3089

Agent www.fldfs.com/data/aar_alis1/

Insurer www.fldfs.com/Consumers/imc.htm
www.fldfs.com/Consumers/small_group_market_carriers.htm

Georgia

Contact www.gainsurance.org/INSURANCE/ConsumerServices.aspx
800-656-2298 / 404-656-2070

Agent www.gainsurance.org/INSURANCE/AgentStatus.aspx

Hawaii

Contact www.hawaii.gov/dcca/areas/ins/consumer/consumer_information/health/
808-586-2790
ihealth@dcca.hawaii.gov

Agent pahoehoe.ehawaii.gov/ils/app

Idaho

Contact www.doi.idaho.gov/Health/healthinfo.aspx
800-721-3272 / 208-334-4250
www.doi.idaho.gov/shiba/dir_mail.asp?did=26

Agent www.doi.idaho.gov/Insurance/search.aspx

Insurer http://www.doi.idaho.gov/Health/individual_list.aspx
http://www.doi.idaho.gov/Health/smempl_list.aspx

Illinois

Contact www.idfpr.com/DOI/HealthInsurance/HealthInsurance.asp
www.idfpr.com/DOI/OCHI/Office_Consumer_Health_Ins.asp
877-527-9431 / 217-782-4515
Director@ins.state.il.us

Agent www.idfpr.com/DOI/Producer/default.asp

Indiana

Contact www.ai.org/idoi/health/
800-622-4461 / 317-232-2395
doi@doi.state.in.us

Agent www.ai.org/idoi/company_producer/licenseSearch.html

Insurer http://www.ai.org/idoi/companyinfo/hmos/index.html
http://www.ai.org/idoi/companyinfo/preferredntwks/index.html

Iowa

Contact www.iid.state.ia.us/about_us/consumer.asp
877-955-1212 / 515-281-5705
www.iid.state.ia.us/contact_us/contactus.asp

Agent https://sbs-ia-public.naic.org/Lion-Web/jsp/sbsreports/AgentLookup.jsp

Kansas

Contact www.ksinsurance.org/consumers/consumer.htm
800-432-2484 / 785-296-3071
commissioner@ksinsurance.org

Agent towerii.ksinsurance.org/agent/agent.jsp?pagnam=agentsearch

Insurer http://www.ksinsurance.org/consumers/majmed.htm

Kentucky

Contact doi.ppr.ky.gov/kentucky/divs.asp?DIVID=5
800-595-6053 / 502-564-6034
Debbie.Stamper@ky.gov;Lori.Cunningham@ky.gov

Agent doi.ppr.ky.gov/Kentucky/search/Agent/

Insurer http://doi.ppr.ky.gov/kentucky/Documents/Health/GroupHealthList091007.pdf
http://doi.ppr.ky.gov/kentucky/Documents/Health/IndividualREV05142007.pdf

Louisiana

Contact www.ldi.state.la.us/Health/index.htm
800-259-5301 / 225-219-4770
skipper@ldi.state.la.us

Agent www.ldi.state.la.us/search_forms/searchforms.htm

Maine

Contact www.maine.gov/pfr/insurance/consumer/index.htm
800-300-5000 / 207-624-8475
Glenn.J.Griswold@maine.gov

Agent www.maine.gov/pfr/insurance/license_search.htm

Insurer http://www.maine.gov/pfr/insurance/consumer/indhlth.htm
http://www.maine.gov/pfr/insurance/employer/smallemp.htm

Maryland

Contact www.mdinsurance.state.md.us/jsp/consumer/Consumer.jsp10?divisionName=Consumer+Information&pageName=/jsp/consumer/Consumer.jsp10
800-492-6116 / 410-468-2000
www.mdinsurance.state.md.us/jsp/Contact.jsp10?selectedSubject=Consumer+Education+%26+Advocacy

Agent mdinsurance3.mdinsurance.state.md.us/iq/jsp/interactiveQuery/ProducerSearch.jsp10?mode=true

Insurer http://www.mdinsurance.state.md.us/jsp/consumer/ConsumerPublications.jsp10?divisionName=Consumer+Publications%5EHealth&pageName=/jsp/consumer/Consumer-Publications.jsp10

Massachusetts

Contact www.mass.gov/?pageID=ocaconstituent&L=2&L0=Home&L1=Consumer&sid=Eoca
617-521-7777 / 413-785-5526
consumer@state.ma.us

Agent www.mass.gov/?pageID=ocaterminal&L=5&L0=Home&L1=Licensee&L2=License
+Types%2c+Forms+%26+Requirements&L3=Insurance&L4=Individual+and+Busi
ness+Entity+Licensing&sid=Eoca&b=terminalcontent&f=doi_Producer_Producer_
list&csid=Eoca

Michigan

Contact www.michigan.gov/cis/0,1607,7-154-10555_12902_35510---,00.html
877-999-6442 / 517-373-0220
ofis-ins-info@michigan.gov

Agent www.dleg.state.mi.us/fis/ind_srch/ins_agnt/insurance_agent_criteria.asp

Insurer www.dleg.state.mi.us/fis/ind_srch/ins_comp/insurance_company_criteria.asp

Minnesota

Contact www.state.mn.us/portal/mn/jsp/content.do?id=-536881350&agency=Commerce
800-657-3602 / 651-296-2488
market.assurance@state.mn.us

Agent www.commerce.state.mn.us/LicenseLookupMain.html

Mississippi

Contact www.doi.state.ms.us/consumer/consumerinfo.htm
800-562-2957 / 601-359-2453
consumer@mid.state.ms.us

Agent www.doi.state.ms.us/licapp/

Insurer http://www.doi.state.ms.us/pdf/hmolist.pdf

Missouri

Contact www.insurance.mo.gov/consumer/index.htm
800-726-7390 / 573-751-2640
consumeraffairs@insurance.mo.gov

Agent www.insurance.mo.gov/consumer/agtstatus.htm

Insurer www.insurance.mo.gov/consumer/hmo/HMOserv.htm

Montana

Contact www.sao.state.mt.us/consumers/index.asp
800-332-6148 / 406-444-2040
stateauditor@mt.gov

Agent www.sao.state.mt.us/insurance/findagent.asp

Nebraska

Contact www.doi.ne.gov/consumer.htm
877-564-7323 / 402-471-0888
consumer_affairs@doi.state.ne.us

Agent www.doi.ne.gov/appointments/search/index.cgi

Insurer http://www.doi.ne.gov/brochure/b_hmo.htm

Nevada

Contact doi.state.nv.us
888-872-3234 / 775-687-4270
cscc@doi.state.nv.us

New

Hampshire

Contact www.nh.gov/insurance/consumer_services/cons_home.htm
800-852-3416 / 603-271-2261
Requests@ins.nh.gov

Agent https://sbs-nh-public.naic.org/Lion-Web/jsp/sbsreports/AgentLookup.jsp

Insurer www.nh.gov/insurance/consumer_services/cons_complists.htm

New Jersey

Contact www.state.nj.us/dobi/consmnu.shtml
800-446-7467 / 609-292-5316
ombudsman@dobi.state.nj.us

Agent https://www6.state.nj.us/DOBI_LicSearch/Jsp/insSearch.jsp

Insurer www.state.nj.us/dobi/reform.htm

New Mexico

Contact www.nmprc.state.nm.us/lhb.htm
www.nmprc.state.nm.us/mhcb.htm
877-673-1732 / 505-827-3928
mhcb.grievance@state.nm.us

New York

Contact www.ins.state.ny.us/chealth.htm
800-342-3736 / 212-480-6400 / 518-474-6600
consumers@ins.state.ny.us

North Carolina

Contact www.ncdoi.com/Consumer/consumer_home.asp
800-546-5664 / 919-807-6750

Agent infoportal.ncdoi.net/agent_search.jsp?TYPE=P

Insurer http://www.ncdoi.com/Consumer/Documents/list_individual_health.PDF
http://www.ncdoi.com/Consumer/Documents/list_small_group_health.PDF

North Dakota

Contact www.nd.gov/ndins/consumer/
800-247-0560 / 701-328-2440

Agent www.nd.gov/ndins/find/

Insurer http://www.nd.gov/ndins/consumer/details.asp?ID=146
http://www.nd.gov/ndins/consumer/details.asp?ID=144

Ohio

Contact www.ohioinsurance.gov/ConsumServ/ConServIndex.asp
800-686-1526 / 614-644-2673
www.ohioinsurance.gov/ConsumServ/ConServComments.htm

Agent www.ohioinsurance.gov/ConsumServ/Ocs/agentloc.asp

Insurer http://www.ohioinsurance.gov/reports/AuthList.pdf

Oklahoma

Contact www.oid.state.ok.us/
800-522-0071 / 405-521-2828
feedback@insurance.state.ok.us

Oregon

Contact www.cbs.state.or.us/external/ins/consumer/consumer.html
503-947-7980
dcbs.insmail@state.or.us

Agent www4.cbs.state.or.us/ex/ins/inslic/agent/index.cfm

Insurer www.cbs.state.or.us/ins/consumer/health-insurance/individual-plans.html
www.cbs.state.or.us/ins/sehi/sehi_companies.html

Pennsylvania

Contact www.ins.state.pa.us/ins/cwp/view.asp?a=1281&Q=544190
877-881-6388 / 717-787-2317
www.insurance.state.pa.us/dsf/inquiry.html

Agent http://164.156.71.30/producer/ilist1.asp

Rhode Island

Contact www.ri.gov/
401-222-5424
HealthInsInquiry@ohic.ri.gov

For Individuals, Rhode Island has Blue Cross/Blue Shield only, but you can choose between being medically underwritten or not.

South Carolina

Contact www.doi.sc.gov/Eng/Public/Consumer/Consumer.aspx
800-768-3467 / 803-737-6180
info@doi.sc.gov

Agent www.doi.sc.gov/Eng/Public/Queries/IndvdlLicSrch.aspx

South Dakota

Contact www.state.sd.us/drr2/reg/insurance/consumer/index.html
605-773-3563
insurance@state.sd.us

Insurer www.state.sd.us/drr2/reg/insurance/consumer/major_med_carriers.html

Tennessee

Contact www.state.tn.us/consumer/
800-342-8385 / 615-741-4737
Consumer.Affairs@state.tn.us

Agent licsrch.state.tn.us/

Insurer http://www.state.tn.us/commerce/insurance/documents/documents_two/
MMCOS060205.pdf

Texas

Contact www.tdi.state.tx.us/consumer/index.html
800-252-3439 / 512-463-6515
PIO@tdi.state.tx.us

Agent www.texasonline.state.tx.us/NASApp/tdi/TdiARManager

Insurer www.tdi.state.tx.us/consumer/colists.html

Utah

Contact www.insurance.utah.gov/consumers.html
866-350-6242 / 801-538-3077
health.uid@utah.gov

Agent https://secure.utah.gov/cas/search?page=searchMenu

Insurer http://www.insurance.utah.gov/2004GovRpt/MS_2004/MS_GroupA&H.pdf
http://www.insurance.utah.gov/2004GovRpt/MS_2004/MS_IndA&H.pdf

Vermont

Contact www.bishca.state.vt.us/HcaDiv/consumer_help/consumer_info_assistance.htm
800-631-7788 / 802-828-2900
publicinfo@bishca.state.vt.us

Virginia

Contact www.scc.virginia.gov/division/boi/webpages/boiconsumer.htm
877-310-6560 / 804-371-9741
bureauofinsurance@scc.virginia.gov

Agent boi.scc.virginia.gov/agentlookup/

Insurer boi.scc.virginia.gov/companylookup/

Washington

Contact www.insurance.wa.gov/consumers/health/healthinsurance.asp
800-562-6900 / 360-725-7080
cad@oic.wa.gov

Agent fortress.wa.gov/oic/laa/LAAMain.aspx

Insurer www.insurance.wa.gov/publications/health/Consumers-Guide-PDFS/All_Health_
Plans.pdf

West Virginia

Contact www.wvinsurance.gov/consumer/consumer_services.htm
888-879-9842 / 304-558-3386
consumer.service@wvinsurance.gov

Agent www.wvinsurance.gov/agent%5Fdetail/

Insurer www.wvinsurance.gov/company/pdf/wv_dom_companies.pdf (see page 2)

Wisconsin

Contact oci.wi.gov/consinfo.htm
800-236-8517 / 608-266-3585
information@oci.state.wi.us

Agent ociaccess.oci.wi.gov/ProducerInfo/PrdInfo.oci

Insurer ociaccess.oci.wi.gov/CmpInfo/CmpInfo.oci

Wyoming

Contact insurance.state.wy.us/index.asp
800-438-5768 / 307-777-7401
wyinsdep@state.wy.us

Agent insurance.state.wy.us/search/search.asp

Insurer Contact DOI

Appendix C

National Survey of Health Insurance Prices

To give you an idea of how much health insurance costs based on the laws of the state that you live in, the following table is provided with the state capital and some of the largest cities. Data is presented for a family of 5: one parent in the early 40's, another in the late 30's, and three children under 18. The table includes the least expensive rate and the most expensive rate for a family that has perfect health, but has choices in the market due to a variety of products to purchase. The average lowest premium for all locations listed in the 50 states (weighted toward some states due to multiple cities within the same state) is $267.60, and the average highest premium $1,289.50. The premiums could be much higher in states that allow medical underwriting if one or more family members had a significant medical condition.

Reading the table is simple – look at a location and you'll see the least expensive and most expensive choices, expressed as a percentage of our nationwide average above. For example, the first line for Montgomery, Alabama, shows that if you live there, your least expensive choice costs about 79% of the average least expensive choice, and your most expensive choice costs 92% of the average for the most expensive choices. This means that Montgomery is a pretty good place to live when you need to buy health insurance. You can glance through the table and see that some locations have less expensive health insurance, and some have more expensive insurance, including Boston, Massachusetts, which has the highest cost for the least expensive choice, and is second only to New York for the highest most expensive rates.

Below the table is a graph created from the table. This is a quick way to see which states have the lowest lows and also the lowest highs, so if you're ever in the process of relocating, you can know ahead of time what it may cost to buy health insurance. Also, if you are planning a move and have a medical condition, be sure to review Figure 2.6 on page 32, which gives the best states in which to buy health insurance if you have a medical condition. When first reading the graph, you may wish to consider comparing only the black bars to other black bars, and the grey bars to only grey bars. Once you've gotten comfortable with the graph, seeing the least and most expensive together makes sense.

It bears repeating that the information here is for the most likely rate that you'll receive, which generally assumes that you are in good health. For those states that have community rating and guaranteed issue, identified in Figure 2.6, quotes are not likely to vary for any medical conditions. It should be noted that the information here was not derived in any scientific manner, but serves as a picture of what the cheapest and most expensive policies cost in the listed locations.

Comparison of Local Rates to Average Rates of Listed Locations

State	City	Zip Code	Lowest Cost Option as percent of average 100% = $267.60	Highest Cost Option as percent of average 100% = $1289.50
Alabama	Montgomery	36101	79%	92%
Alaska	Anchorage	99501	107	156
Alaska	Juneau	99801	107	156
Arizona	Phoenix	85025	72	61
Arkansas	Little Rock	72201	74	68
California	Los Angeles	90001	115	78
California	Sacramento	95814	141	65
California	San Diego	92101	106	70
California	San Jose	95101	134	63
California	San Francisco	94102	134	63
Colorado	Denver	80012	76	63
Connecticut	Hartford	06101	74	75
Delaware	Dover	19901	91	67
District of Columbia	Washington	20016	67	69
Florida	Jacksonville	32099	72	87
Florida	Tallahassee	32301	66	71
Georgia	Atlanta	30303	87	86
Hawaii	Honolulu	96813	41	172
Idaho	Boise	83702	62	70
Illinois	Chicago	60601	113	83
Illinois	Springfield	62701	89	68
Indiana	Indianapolis	46201	95	86
Iowa	Des Moines	50307	60	58
Kansas	Topeka	66603	96	71
Kentucky	Frankfort	40601	65	39
Louisiana	Baton Rouge	70801	81	82
Maine	Augusta	04330	308	133
Maryland	Annapolis	21401	87	55
Maryland	Baltimore	21201	87	55
Massachusetts	Boston	02108	363	292
Michigan	Detroit	48201	87	74
Michigan	Lansing	48906	66	64
Minnesota	St. Paul	55101	119	115
Mississippi	Jackson	39201	103	91

State	City	Zip Code	Lowest Cost Option as percent of average 100% = $267.60	Highest Cost Option as percent of average 100% = $1289.50
Missouri	Jefferson City	65101	82%	62%
Montana	Helena	59601	126	99
Nebraska	Lincoln	68502	99	73
Nevada	Carson City	89701	139	99
New Hampshire	Concord	03301	66	120
New Jersey	Trenton	08608	147	286
New Mexico	Santa Fe	87501	70	78
New York	Albany	12202	73	353
New York	New York	10001	152	301
North Carolina	Charlotte	28202	93	97
North Carolina	Raleigh	27601	85	89
North Dakota	Bismarck	58501	24	75
Ohio	Columbus	43085	72	50
Oklahoma	Oklahoma City	73102	84	88
Oregon	Salem	97301	108	49
Pennsylvania	Harrisburg	17101	86	84
Pennsylvania	Philadelphia	19102	155	83
Rhode Island	Providence	02903	58	144
South Carolina	Columbia	29201	101	80
South Dakota	Pierre	57501	57	191
Tennessee	Memphis	38103	93	58
Tennessee	Nashville	37201	86	62
Texas	Austin	78701	84	59
Texas	Fort Worth	76102	104	59
Texas	Houston	77002	113	59
Texas	San Antonio	78201	92	56
Utah	Salt Lake City	84101	61	61
Vermont	Montpelier	05602	156	257
Virginia	Richmond	23219	72	70
Washington	Olympia	98501	153	63
Washington	Seattle	98101	153	63
West Virginia	Charleston	25301	98	261
Wisconsin	Madison	53703	84	73
Wyoming	Cheyenne	82001	48	101

Graph of National Survey of Health Insurance Prices for a Family of 5

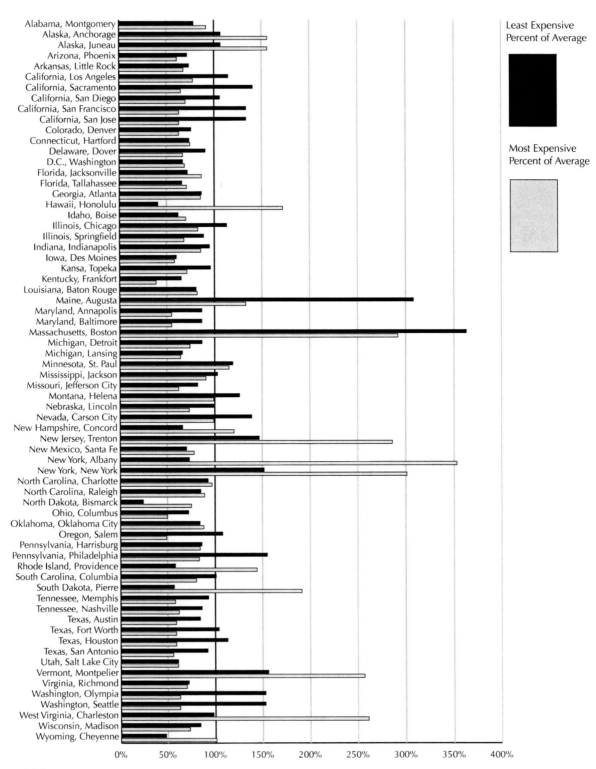

Least Expensive
Percent of Average

Most Expensive
Percent of Average

Appendix D

Glossary

Agent – A person licensed by the state to sell insurance who represents one or more insurance companies. They are paid commissions by the insurance company to sell insurance products to you.

AHIA – Association of Health Insurance Advisors, a health insurance division of the National Association of Insurance and Financial Advisors (NAIFA).

Annual Limit – The maximum amount the insurer will pay in a plan year. Your insurance benefits run out when you exceed this amount in any plan year.

Association Group Insurance – An insurance policy issued to an association that is sold to members of the association, who are issued certificates of coverage.

Certificate of Coverage – A document that is issued to an insured person who takes insurance through a group plan. The policy is issued to the group owner (employer or association), and the certificate contains only some of the information of the policy. The certificate holder has fewer rights than a policy holder.

CFP – Certified Financial Planner, a designation that indicates education, experience, and examination in financial planning.

Claim – Any time that you use your health insurance you make a claim for benefits.

COBRA – The Consolidated Omnibus Budget Reconciliation Act, U.S. federal legislation that provides for continuation of group health insurance when you leave employment.

Coinsurance – A split between what you pay and the insurance company pays for a dollar amount, usually expressed as a dollar amount and a percentage.

Community Rating – Each person in the community pays the same amount for health insurance, regardless of health status. It is typically modified to include things like location within a state.

Copayment / Copay – A fixed dollar amount paid for services. This can include a doctor visit, a specialist visit, a prescription, or other.

Coverages – Dollar amounts and features for which the insurer will pay eligible expenses.

Deductible – An amount that the insured pays before the insurer starts paying for expenses. Copays and ineligible expenses are not included when calculating this amount.

Discount – In a network, the amount that the insurer has negotiated with the provider to reduce fees.

Eligible Expense – Will be paid or included in the deductible or coinsurance by the insurer. Also, separately, eligible for tax treatment and payment by HSA funds.

Employer Group Insurance – Group health insurance issued to an employer under which employees may be covered and issued a certificate of coverage.

EOB – Explanation of Benefits, sent to you after the claim has been processed by the insurer.

Exclusion – Medical procedures, treatments, etc., that are specifically not covered under the policy.

FSA – Flexible Spending Account.

Gaps in Coverage – Expenses that are not covered, or dollar ranges at which there is no coverage.

Guaranteed Issue – You will not be rejected for any reason. However, the rate may be higher for medical conditions.

Guaranteed Renewable – If you continue to pay premiums and stay in your location the policy will continue year after year instead of requiring renewal and underwriting each year.

ERISA – Employee Retirement Income Security Act.

HDHP – High Deductible Health Plan, a type of insurance policy which, when it meets certain other qualifications, allows you to open a tax advantaged Health Savings Account.

HIA – Health Insurance Associate.

HIPAA – Health Insurance Portability and Accountability Act.

HMO – Health Maintenance Organization.

HR – Human Resources.

HRA – Health Reimbursement Account.

HSA – Health Savings Account, potentially "triple tax free" in deposits, growth, and withdrawals for allowable health expenses.

In-Force – The way that you keep your health insurance active.

Indemnity – Traditional type of insurance where you choose the doctor and facility and are reimbursed for expenses according to policy, after receiving treatment.

Individual Insurance – Insurance purchased by an individual rather than a group.

IRA – Individual Retirement Account.

IRS – Internal Revenue Service.

Lifetime Limit – A dollar limit at which the insurance policy will no longer pay claims.

Major Medical – Comprehensive insurance, usually meaning an indemnity policy.

Managed Care – When you are restricted to a set of doctors/facilities in a network, with some possible provisions to go outside of the network.

Medicaid – A government program that covers medical expenses of those in poverty.

Medical Condition – Something that is either an on-going problem or significant and happened in the past for which underwriting may reject or increase rates.

Medical Event – An occasion when something medically significant happens, such as breaking a limb or being diagnosed with a condition.

Medical Underwriting – The plan uses your medical history to determine whether you are insurable and how much they will charge.

Medicare – A government program that covers eligible people over 65 and some people with disabilities.

Members – Health insurers use this term to refer to their customers.

MEWA – Multiple Employer Welfare Arrangements.

MIB – Medical Information Bureau, a consumer reporting company that collects information on the health status of people.

MSA – Medical Savings Account.

MHP – Managed Healthcare Professional.

NAHU – National Association of Health Underwriters.

NAIC – National Association of Insurance Commissioners.

NAIFA – National Association of Insurance and Financial Advisors.

NCQA – National Committee for Quality Assurance compiles information about managed care health insurance.

Network – A set of facilities that when used provides a preferential cost to the insured.

Out-of-Pocket – Defined by the insurance companies as the amount that you must pay before they pay for everything. Their definition is not clear because you pay premiums too, and they won't pay for anything after your annual or lifetime maximums have been met.

Paramedical Examination – A physical examination that will be used in conjunction with an application for underwriting.

Plan – Not necessarily synonymous with policy, but many insurers refer to their choices as plans.

Policy – A legal document giving certain rights to the purchaser. Not the same as a certificate.

POS – Point of Service.

PPO – Preferred Provider Plan.

Pre-Existing Condition – A condition that the insurer will not cover for a period of time and/or for which they may increase your premium.

Pre-Certification – Some insurers require that you verify that they'll pay for big procedures so that you don't get medical care that isn't covered.

Premium – The amount that you pay periodically to keep your health insurance in-force.

Private Insurance – Insurance purchased from an insurance company as opposed to purchasing it from the government or self insuring.

Quote – Usually the most likely amount paid by someone with your general characteristics (age, weight, etc.).

Rainy-Day Fund – An amount of money usually held in a savings account equal to several months to a year of living expenses that can be used when something goes wrong.

Rating – How much you will pay for insurance given your medical underwriting status and the local costs and claims amount.

Reasonable and Customary – An amount that an insurer will pay, leaving you the rest of the bill. Too frequently it is less than your doctor or facility charges.

Re-Underwriting – Also known as post claim underwriting. After you have made claims on the policy or needed significant medical care, the insurer changes the rating and premium on your policy. Illegal many places, currently out of favor elsewhere.

REBC – Registered Employee Benefits Consultant.

RHU – Registered Health Underwriter.

Rider – A change to an insurance policy that "rides" along with the policy and usually excludes care for a certain condition, for a fixed or unlimited period of time.

SCHIP – State Children's Health Insurance Program.

Small Business Group Insurance – A group insurance policy issued to a small company or sole proprietor of a business that has a minimum of 1 or 2 employees, and a maximum of 50, depending on state law.

Underwriting – The process of evaluating the information on an insurance application and any additional supporting documentation to determine whether coverage will be offered and the premium that will be charged.

Up-Rate – Meaning that you will pay more money in premiums each month.

Wellness – Also known as preventative care. Care received to prevent medical conditions from occurring in the first place.

Index

Ordering Information

Get a Good Deal on Your Health Insurance Without Getting Ripped-Off

You may order copies of our books directly from Aji Publishing,
or through your favorite book retailer.

Order By Computer:

Go to www.AjiBooks.com to order copies.

Don't forget to visit www.BestHealthInsuranceBook.com too!

Order By Telephone:

Call us at 877-257-6876 or 919-338-1863.

We're happy to take credit card orders by telephone.

Order By Mail:

Make checks payable to Aji Publishing.

Send pre-paid orders to:

Aji Publishing

P.O. Box 2207

Chapel Hill, NC 27515-2207

Include $17.95 per copy plus tax for North Carolina addresses.

Please add $5.00 for shipping and handling to each address.

Multiple copy orders only pay $5.00 per address.

For international orders, please contact us for further details.

Be sure to include your name, address, city, state, zip code, email,
and a telephone number.

Visit our website at: www.AjiBooks.com for additional book titles.

www.AjiBooks.com   877.257.6876

Printed in the United States
216684BV00002B/6/A